Radio Propagation Explained

Steve Nichols, G0KYA

Edited, expanded and updated from original
material by Ian Poole, G3YWX

Radio Society of Great Britain

Published by: Radio Society of Great Britain, 3 Abbey Court, Priory Business Park, Bedford, MK44 3WH, United Kingdom www.rsgb.org

First Published 2016

Reprinted 2018 & 2020

Reprinted digitally 2023 onwards

ISBN 9781 9101 9328 0

Publisher's note
The opinions expressed in this book are those of the author and not necessarily those of the RSGB. While the information presented is believed to be correct, the author, the publisher and their agents cannot accept responsibility for consequences arising from any inaccuracies or omissions.

Production: Mark Allgar, M1MPA

Cover design: Kevin Williams, M6CYB

Typography: Steve Telenius-Lowe, PJ4DX

Printed in Great Britain by 4Edge Ltd. of Hockley, Essex

Contents

Foreword

Welcome to this RSGB book on radio propagation, a subject that has fascinated me from a time before I was even licensed. I still think it is magical how low-power signals can travel from one side of the planet to the other. And while we now understand the process by which they get from A to B, we still can't accurately predict how successful our HF communications will be on a day-to-day basis – there are just too many variables.

Nevertheless, armed with a basic knowledge of ionospheric propagation, the latest solar data and perhaps a propagation prediction program, we can now calculate the probability of making a contact on a particular band and choose our operating times accordingly.

This is a far cry from the very early days of radio, when pioneers like Marconi had little or no idea how signals were propagated. When his signals crossed the Atlantic from Poldhu in Cornwall to St John's in Newfoundland in 1901, Marconi knew that they were either passing through the Earth (which seemed unlikely), were somehow following its curvature, or they were being reflected from an invisible mirror in the sky.

In fact the early seeds for what was later coined ionospheric propagation had been sown a lot earlier. In 1839 German mathematician and scientist Carl Friedrich Gauss had first speculated that the upper atmosphere might contain a conducting layer. And in 1878 Scottish physicist Balfour Stewart again postulated the existence of a conductive layer in the upper atmosphere to explain variations that were being observed in the Earth's magnetic field.

The big leap forward came in 1902 – one year after Marconi first spanned the Atlantic – when Arthur E Kennelly and Oliver Heaviside both independently suggested that Marconi's signals were propagated by reflection from an ionised layer in the upper atmosphere. It took a further 22 years until its existence was confirmed by British scientist Edward V Appleton in 1924, for which he received the Nobel Prize for Physics in 1947.

After that, extensive research was undertaken to understand better what was going on at the edge of space.

In 1926 Americans Gregory Breit and Merle Tuve first used a pulse technique to measure the heights and critical frequencies of a number of ionospheric layers. Their's was the first true ionosonde, and may have been the first application of what was to become known later as radar.

But we mustn't just focus on the ionosphere. VHF enthusiasts are more interested in how radio waves propagate through the troposphere. When I was first licensed in the early 1980s I spent many happy hours sitting on a cardboard box in my parent's loft. I had a two-and-a-half watt Yaesu FT-290R for 2m (144MHz) and a small four-element quad beam sitting next to me. If the weather conditions were right, with high pressure, I found I could talk to other radio amateurs around the country from my home in Norfolk, and even get as far afield as the south of France, the Netherlands, Germany, Norway and Sweden.

The theory of how tropospheric lifts, ducts and temperature inversions aided VHF propagation was foreign to me – but it didn't stop me having a lot of fun. And that's what this book aims to do – give you a good grounding in radio propagation principles and so help maximise the fun factor for your radio hobby.

The base text of this book is from Ian Poole's, G3YWX, excellent *Radio Propagation – Principles and Practice*, first published in 2004. I've revised it with new, updated information and some new chapters.

We look at the Sun, HF and VHF propagation, as well as how tools like solar data, weather forecasts, propagation prediction software and much more can help you. It includes the latest ideas on how sporadic E forms every summer to give long-distance contacts on the upper HF and the VHF bands. Plus there's a chapter on LF and MF propagation and what you can do with the lowest bands in our radio amateurs' arsenal.

We also look at satellite communications and earth-moon-earth, or EME, contacts for those of you who think propagation is really out of this world. Above all, we want to set you on a course to understand radio propagation better. It is still a field where radio amateurs have a lot to contribute. In the past radio amateurs have contributed to our knowledge of auroral propagation, sporadic E, and much more.

We certainly don't know everything there is to know about radio propagation and you could still help further that knowledge with your own research.

Steve Nichols, G0KYA
September 2016

Chapter 1

Electromagnetic waves

Radio waves or signals are a form of *electromagnetic wave*. Accordingly, an understanding of the nature of such waves is a key element in being able to discover how radio waves propagate. As they travel, the radio waves are affected in different ways. Even moving through free space they decrease in amplitude as the signal spreads out. If they travel though the Earth's atmosphere they can be affected by it in a way which is governed by the nature of the waves and how they interact with their surroundings.

All electromagnetic waves consist of two elements: an electric and a magnetic component and these are inextricably linked. However, before examining the combined electromagnetic wave it is worth taking a look at electric and magnetic fields.

Electric fields

An electric field is associated with *electric charges*. Any electrically charged object, whether it has a static charge associated with it or whether it is has an electric potential and is carrying a current, will have an electric field associated with it.

There are a number of properties associated with charges. It is commonly known that like charges repel one another and opposite charges attract. This can be demonstrated in various ways and it can often be seen in everyday life. For example, hair often stands on end after it has been brushed or combed because the hairs have the same charge on them and tend to repel one another. Examples like these are quite fun to demonstrate and occur because the voltages that are involved are very high and may typically rise to values of many kilovolts. However, even the comparatively low voltages that are found in electronic circuits exhibit the same effects, although to a much smaller degree.

Any object that has a charge, whether static or dynamic, will have an associated potential and an associated electric field. The electric field radiates out from the object with an electric potential, falling away as the distance from it is increased. Take the example of a charged sphere with a potential of 10V. At the surface of the sphere the electrostatic potential is 10V but, as the distance from the sphere is increased, this potential starts to fall. It can be

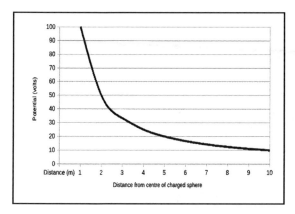

Fig 1.1: Variation of potential with distance from the charged sphere.

seen that it is possible to draw lines of equal potential around the sphere. The potential falls away as the distance is increased from the sphere, and it can be shown that the value reduces as the inverse of the distance. eg doubling the distance halves the potential. The variation of potential with distance from the sphere is shown in **Fig 1.1**.

The electric field gives the direction and magnitude of the force on a charged object. The *field intensity* is the negative value of the slope in **Fig 1.1**. This means that the steeper the slope, the greater the field intensity, and the negative value results from the fact that the slope is falling on the graph. The slope of a curve plotted on a graph is the rate of change of a variable. In this case it represents the rate of change of the potential with distance at a particular point. This is known as the *potential gradient*, and varies as the inverse square of the distance. In other words, doubling the distance reduces the potential gradient by a factor of four.

Magnetic fields

Like electric fields, *magnetic fields* are also important and it is possible to draw many similarities between them. As already mentioned, electric charges attract and repel one another and so do their magnetic equivalents. Analogous to the positive and negative charges, magnets have two types of pole, namely a *north pole* and a *south pole*. Like poles repel and dissimilar ones attract. In the case of magnets it is also found that the magnetic field strength falls away, reducing as the inverse square of the distance.

The first magnets to be discovered were permanent magnets. After dynamic electricity was discovered and came into use it was noticed that there was a magnetic field associated with the current. This was detected by the fact that a compass needle placed close to the conductor was deflected. The lines of force are in a particular direction around the wire as shown in **Fig 1.2**. An easy method of determining which way they go around the conductor is to use the *corkscrew rule*. Imagine a right-handed corkscrew being driven into a cork on the direction of the current flow. The lines of force will be in the direction of rotation of the corkscrew.

Fig 1.2: Lines of magnetic force around a current-carrying conductor.

Radio waves

As already mentioned, radio waves are a form of electromagnetic wave. They consist of the same type of radiation as light, ultra-violet, infra-red etc, differing only in the wavelength or frequency of the radiation. The waves have both electric and magnetic components that are inseparable. The planes of the fields are at right-angles to each other and to the direction in which the wave is travelling. The wave can be visualised as shown in **Fig 1.3**.

It is useful to see where the different elements of the wave emanate from. The electric component of the wave results from the voltage changes that occur as the antenna element is excited by the alternating waveform. The lines of force in the electric field run along the same axis as the antenna, but spreading out as they move away from it. This electric field is measured in terms of the change of potential over a given distance, eg volts per metre, and this is known as the *field strength*.

The other component, namely the magnetic field, is at right-angles to the electric field and hence it is at right-angles to the plane of the antenna. It is generated as a result of the current flow in the antenna.

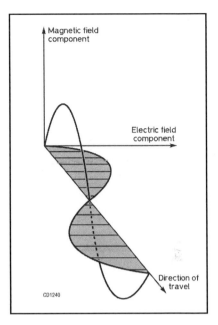

Fig 1.3: An electromagnetic wave.

Wavelength, frequency and velocity

There are a number of basic properties of electromagnetic waves, or any repetitive waves for that matter, that are particularly important. The first is the *wavelength*, which is the distance between a given point on one cycle and the same point on the next cycle as shown in **Fig 1.4**. The easiest points to choose are the peaks as these are the simplest to locate. The wavelength was used in the early days of radio to determine the position of a signal on the dial of a set. Although it is not used for this purpose today, it is nevertheless an important feature of any signal. The position of a signal on the dial of a radio set or its position within the radio spectrum is now determined by its frequency as this provides a more accurate and convenient method for determining the properties of the signal.

The second property of the electromagnetic wave is its *frequency*. This is the number of times a particular point on the wave moves up and

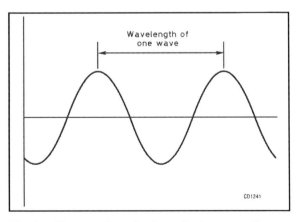

Fig 1.4: The wavelength of an electromagnetic wave.

down in a given time (normally a second). The unit of frequency is the *hertz* and it is equal to one cycle per second. This unit is named after the German scientist who discovered radio waves.

The frequencies used in radio are usually very high. Accordingly the prefixes 'kilo', 'mega', and 'giga' are often seen. 1kHz is a thousand hertz, 1MHz is a million hertz, and 1GHz is a thousand million hertz, ie 1000MHz. Originally the unit of frequency was not given a name and *cycles per second* (c/s) were used. Some older books may show these units together with their prefixes ('kc/s', 'Mc/s' etc) for higher frequencies.

The third major property of the wave is its *speed*. Radio waves travel at the same speed as light. For most practical purposes this speed is taken to be 300 million metres per second (in a vacuum) although a more exact value is 299,792,500m/s.

Frequency-to-wavelength conversion

The frequency and the wavelength are related to each other and it is very easy to determine the frequency of a signal if the wavelength is known, and vice versa if the frequency is known. The two are related to one another by the speed of the signal as shown:

$$\lambda = \frac{c}{f}$$

where λ is the wavelength in metres, f is the frequency in hertz and c is the speed of radio waves in a vacuum (light), taken as 300,000,000m/s for all practical purposes.

As an example it can be seen that a signal with a wavelength of 300m has a frequency of 300,000,000/300 or one million hertz, ie 1MHz.

Electromagnetic and radio spectrum

Electromagnetic waves have an enormous range, and as a result it is very convenient to see where each of the different forms of radiation fits within the spectrum as a whole. It can be seen that radio signals have the lowest frequency and hence the longest wavelengths. Above the radio spectrum other forms of radiation exist, including infra-red radiation, light, ultra-violet and a number of others as shown in **Fig 1.5**.

Even within the radio spectrum there is an enormous range of frequencies which extends over many decades. In order to be able to categorise the

Fig 1.5: The electromagnetic wave spectrum.

different areas and reduce these to more manageable sizes, the spectrum is divided into different segments as shown.

Polarisation

Apart from the frequency, wavelength and speed of an electromagnetic wave, there are many other parameters it possesses that are of importance. One of these is its *polarisation*. In essence this defines the plane in which the wave is vibrating. As electromagnetic waves consist of an electric and a magnetic field vibrating at right-angles to each other, it is necessary to adopt a convention to determine the polarisation of the signal. For this purpose the plane of the electric field is used.

The polarisation of a signal is important for a number of reasons. The first is that antennas are sensitive to polarisation. For most antennas it is easy to determine the polarisation because it is simply that of the plane of the elements in the antenna. In other words, an antenna with vertical elements will receive vertically polarised signals best, and an antenna with horizontal elements will receive horizontally polarised signals best.

Vertical and horizontal polarisations are the most straightforward and most commonly used forms and they fall into a category known as *linear polarisation*. However, this is not the only form as it is possible to generate waveforms that have *circular polarisation*.

Circular polarisation can be visualised by imagining a signal propagating from an antenna that is rotating. The tip of the electric field vector can be seen to trace out a helix or corkscrew as it travels away from the antenna. Circular polarisation can be either right- or left-handed, dependent upon the direction of rotation as seen from the transmitting antenna.

It is also possible to obtain *elliptical polarisation*. This occurs when there is a combination of both linear and circular polarisation. Again this can be visualised by imagining the tip of the electric field tracing out an elliptically shaped corkscrew.

The polarisation of a signal is very important. An antenna receiving a signal will produce the largest output when the incoming signal has the same polarisation as the antenna. This means that in free space both the transmitting and receiving antennas should have the same polarisation (ie be in the same plane) to produce the best signal at the receiving antenna. In theory, if the antennas are linearly polarised and are at right-angles to each other (ie *cross-polarised*) then the output from the receiving antenna should be zero. A similar situation exists for circular polarisation where cross-polarised antennas will produce no output. In other words, a left-handed antenna will not give an output when a right-handed circularly polarised signal appears.

However, it is possible for linearly polarised antennas to receive circularly polarised signals and vice versa. The strength will be equal whether the linearly polarised antenna is mounted vertically, horizontally or in any other plane but directed towards the arriving signal. There will be some degradation because the signal level will be 3dB less than if a circularly polarised antenna of the same sense was used. The same situation exists when a circularly polarised antenna receives a linearly polarised signal.

For terrestrial applications it is found that once a signal has been transmitted its polarisation will remain broadly the same. However, reflections from objects in the path can change the polarisation. As the received signal is the sum of the direct signal plus a number of reflected signals the overall polarisation of the signal can change slightly although it usually remains broadly the same. When reflections take place from the ionosphere, greater changes may occur. In fact, any radio wave that has been reflected off the ionosphere will become an elliptically-polarised wave.

Different types of polarisation are used in different applications as appropriate. Linear polarisation is by far the most widely used. Vertical polarisation is often used for mobile or point-to-point applications. This is because many vertical antennas have an omni-directional radiation pattern and it means that the antennas do not have to be re-orientated as positions are changed if for example they are on a moving vehicle. For other applications the polarisation is often determined by antenna considerations. Some large multi-element antenna arrays can be mounted in a horizontal plane more easily than in the vertical plane. This is because the antenna elements are at right-angles to the vertical tower or pole on which they are mounted and therefore by using an antenna with horizontal elements there is less physical and electrical interference between the two. This determines the standard polarisation in many cases.

In some applications there are performance differences between horizontal and vertical polarisation. For example, medium-wave broadcast stations generally use vertical polarisation because ground-wave propagation over the Earth is considerably better using vertical polarisation, whereas horizontal polarisation shows a marginal improvement for long-distance communications using the ionosphere. Circular polarisation is sometimes used for satellite communications as there are some advantages in terms of propagation and in overcoming the fading caused if the satellite is changing its orientation.

Refraction, reflection and diffraction

As radio signals travel they interact with objects and changes within the media in which they travel. As they do this the signals can undergo reflections, refraction and diffraction in the same way that occurs for light. There are some slight differences as a result of the different wavelengths but the same principles hold true in exactly the same way.

The *reflection* of light is an everyday occurrence and seen in mirrors and glass windows. Radio waves are similarly reflected by many surfaces.

When reflection occurs, it can be seen that the angle of incidence is equal to the angle of reflection for a conducting surface as would be expected for light (**Fig 1.6**), and there is

Direction of incident wave

Direction of reflected wave

θ_i θ_r

Angle of incidence (θ_i) = Angle of reflection (θ_r)

Fig 1.6: Reflection of an electromagnetic wave.

normally some loss, either through absorption or as a result of some of the signal passing into the medium.

For radio signals surfaces such as the sea provide very good reflecting surfaces. Desert areas are poor reflectors and other types of land fall in between these two extremes. In general, though, wet areas provide better reflectors.

It is also possible for radio waves to be *refracted*. The concept of light waves being refracted is very familiar, especially as it can be easily demonstrated by placing a part of a stick or pole in water and leaving the remaining section in air. It is possible to see the apparent change or bend as the stick enters the water. Mirag-

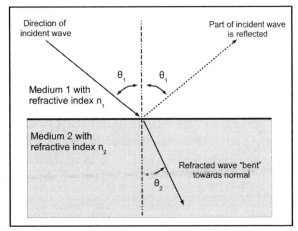

Fig 1.7: Refraction of an electromagnetic wave at the boundary between two areas of differing refractive index.

es also demonstrate refraction and a very similar phenomenon can be noticed on hot days when a shimmering effect can be seen when looking along a straight road. Radio waves are affected in the same way (**Fig 1.7**).

The direction of an electromagnetic wave changes as it moves from an area of one refractive index to another. The angle of incidence and the angle of refraction are linked by *Snell's law* which states:

$$n_1 \sin \theta_1 = n_2 \sin \theta_2$$

For radio signals there are comparatively few instances where the signals move abruptly from a region with one refractive index to a region with another. It is far more common for there to be a comparatively gradual change. This causes the direction of the signal to bend rather than undergo an immediate change in direction.

Radio signals may also undergo *diffraction*. When signals encounter an obstacle they tend to travel around them as shown in **Fig 1.8**, and this can mean that a signal may be received from a transmitter even though it may be 'shaded' by a large object between them. To understand how this happens it is necessary to look at *Huygen's principle*. This states that each point on a spherical wavefront can be con-

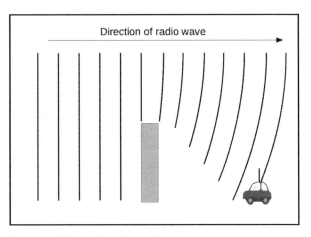

Fig 1.8: Diffraction of a radio signal around an obstacle.

sidered as a source of a secondary wavefront. Even though there will be a shadow zone immediately behind the obstacle, the signal will diffract around the obstacle and start to fill the void. Diffraction is more pronounced when the obstacle becomes sharper and more like a 'knife edge'. For a radio signal a mountain ridge may provide a sufficiently sharp edge, while a more rounded hill will not produce such a marked effect. Low-frequency signals diffract more markedly than higher-frequency ones, and it is for this reason that signals on the long-wave band are able to provide coverage even in hilly or mountainous terrain where signals at VHF and higher would not.

Doppler shift

Doppler shifts occur on sound waves and the same is true for electromagnetic waves, and in particular radio waves. The original effect was established by Doppler in 1842 and relates to frequency changes caused when transmitters or receivers move.

An example is the siren of an ambulance or police car that passes by the listener. As the vehicle comes towards the listener the siren appears to be high in frequency, falling as it passes the listener and moves away. It occurs because when the vehicle is moving towards the listener the waves are compressed and the apparent frequency is increased. Then, as the vehicle moves away, the sound signals are expanded, resulting in a decrease in the apparent frequency.

The same effect occurs with radio waves, often being observed when the reflective medium is moved. When this occurs the signal waves are compressed or expanded in exactly the same way, resulting in a perceived change in frequency.

Signals in free space

In the simplest scenario, radio signals may be considered to travel outwards from the point where they are radiated by an antenna. A rather useful two-dimensional analogy is that of a stone being dropped into water and the resulting circular ripples that move away from the source. As they move outwards they reduce in level, and finally disappear to the eye. In the case of radio signals they spread out in all directions as if on the surface of a sphere and reduce in strength because the area of the sphere is increasing as they travel further away from the source. This form of propagation is called *free space propagation* because there are no external influences on the signal.

The signal reduces in strength and it can be shown that it falls in proportion to the radius squared, and hence the signal strength is inversely proportional to the distance squared from the transmitter to the receiver. This is written mathematically as $1/d^2$, where d is the distance from the transmitter. This means that at a distance 2m from the transmitter, the signal strength is equal to a quarter of the strength that it is at 1m distance; and at 100m, it is only one-ten thousandth of the strength.

Sometimes terrestrial signal paths may approximate to free space transmissions, especially over short distances. This may be the case for short-range 'walkie-talkies' or items such as mobile phones that would not use communications over long distances. However, even these are subject to greater levels of attenuation than would be suggested by the basic calculations because the signals are absorbed by vegetation, buildings or other objects that may fall within the transmission path.

Field strength

Measurements or calculations of the strength of an electromagnetic wave sometimes need to be made. The intensity of a radio wave at any point in space may be expressed in terms of the strength of its electric field. This is expressed in terms of the electric force between points spaced one metre apart, ie volts per metre.

Fig 1.9: Field strength levels from an omni-directional antenna radiating into free space.

CD1243

As an electromagnetic wave travels away from the antenna it spreads out over an increasing area. Under free space conditions it is easy to calculate what the signal strength will be because the signal follows an inverse square-law relationship. In other words, if the distance doubles the signal decays by a factor of two squared or four.

Fig 1.9 shows the calculated field strength levels when a transmitter radiates a signal into free space. If the antenna has a gain this can be easily transferred on to the graph to give the correct levels.

Signals encountered by radio amateurs and listeners will not completely follow the free space calculations because of the Earth itself as well as other objects in or close to the signal path. Conditions in the atmosphere, in particular the troposphere and the ionosphere, also have a significant effect. This makes it more difficult to predict the signal strength at a given point. Calculating the field strength of a signal is normally of little use on its own. It is the actual signal voltage at the input of the receiver that is needed.

Assuming that the antenna for the receiving system is a half-wave dipole, the voltage input can be calculated from

$$V = \frac{48.7 \times E}{f}$$

where V is the voltage at the input of the receiver in microvolts, E is the field strength at the antenna in microvolts per metre and f is the frequency of operation.

If another type of antenna is used, its gain or loss can be used to modify the answer. In other words, if the antenna has a gain of 6dB over a dipole this represents a voltage increase by a factor of two and the answer can be adjusted accordingly. With knowledge of the performance of the radio receiver it is possible to determine whether the signal will be sufficiently strong to copy.

Path loss

In many calculations it is necessary to determine the loss in a given path. Whilst it is not always easy to accurately determine the loss via an ionospheric path because of the great number of variables, paths in free space can be calculated quite accurately. It is common to calculate the path loss to and from a satellite. With the enormous distances to satellites in geostationary orbit (at altitudes of 35,860km above the equator) losses caused purely by the distances involved are very large. By having a knowledge of the path loss, it is possible to optimise the requirements for receiver sensitivity, antenna gains and transmitter power. These are particularly important because increasing the transmitter power or the antenna size at the satellite can be very costly.

The loss can be calculated from the formula:

$$\text{Loss (dB)} = 32.45 + 20 \log_{10} f + 20 \log_{10} d$$

where f is the frequency in megahertz and d is the path distance in kilometres.

Notice that the loss increases with frequency. Fortunately antenna gains can be increased more easily at higher frequencies as antenna sizes are smaller, and this can be used to compensate this effect.

This means that, if someone was directly below a satellite in geostationary orbit, the signal loss to the satellite at a frequency of 10GHz would be:

$$= 32.45 + 20 \log_{10}(10000) + 20 \log_{10}(35860)$$
$$= 32.45 + 20 \times 4 + 20 \times 4.55$$
$$= 203.45dB$$

In view of this enormous loss geostationary satellite systems need to be carefully designed to ensure that a sufficiently good signal can be received.

Systems using satellites in a lower orbit are not nearly as critical because path losses can be very much lower.

Multi-path signals

Very few terrestrial signals that are sent and received travel over a simple single straight path. Instead signals usually arrive at the receiver over a variety of paths and the overall received signal is the sum of several signals. This situation arises because they travel out in a variety of directions and are reflected by objects including buildings, hills, and other objects as shown in **Fig 1.10**. Even the Earth reflects the signal.

Often this type of scenario is referred to as *multi-path propagation*, and it gives rise to phenomena such as the deep fading and distortion that sometimes arises on broadcast FM signals. As the path length for each of these signals is slightly different, it means that they take a different time to arrive

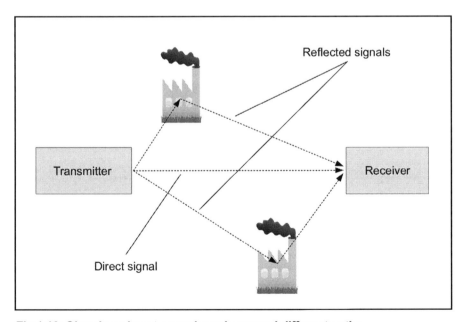

Fig 1.10: Signals arrive at a receiver via several different paths.

at the receiver and will arrive with a different phase. Accordingly they sometimes add together, while at other times they subtract. It is for this reason that VHF and UHF hand-held transceivers only need to move a few centimetres for signal strengths to vary very considerably. As wavelengths are comparatively short, path differences do not have to be that large for signals to arrive in antiphase.

Modes of propagation

Although many of the properties of radio signals which have been mentioned in this chapter relate to the idealised situation when the signal is not modified by external influences, this is not the case for most circumstances. The signals are affected in a number of ways, and this governs the way they travel. At some frequencies they may only travel over short distances whereas at others they may be heard over distances of many thousands of kilometres. The way in which signals propagate can be split into four main categories as detailed below.

The most obvious form of propagation is *free space propagation*. Here the radio signals travel in free space, or away from other objects which influence the way in which they travel. It is only the distance from the source which affects the way in which the field strength reduces. This type of propagation is encountered with signals travelling to and from satellites.

The second type is where signals travel via *ground-wave propagation*. When signals travel as a ground wave they are modified by the ground or terrain over which they travel. They also tend to follow the Earth's curvature. Signals heard on the medium-wave band during the day use this form of propagation.

The third type is called *ionospheric propagation*. Here the radio signals are modified and influenced by the action of the free electrons in the upper reaches of the Earth's atmosphere called the *ionosphere*. This form of propagation is used by stations on the short-wave bands for their signals to be heard around the globe.

Finally there is *tropospheric propagation*. Here the signals are influenced by the variations of refractive index in the troposphere just above the Earth's surface. Tropospheric propagation is often the means by which signals at VHF and above are heard over extended distances.

Chapter 2

The atmosphere

The atmosphere is not only crucial in enabling life to be supported on Earth but it also has a major effect on radio signals. It can change their direction, enabling them to be heard over much greater distances than would otherwise be possible. It also has other effects such as introducing additional loss in some instances or possibly changing the polarisation.

The atmosphere is the gaseous envelope that surrounds the surface of the Earth, and is generally considered to extend to an altitude of around 9500km or 6000 miles. However, at its very outer reaches it is exceedingly thin and the density of the gas is extremely low. In fact the density of the air in the

Fig 2.1. The Earth viewed from space, taken by an Expedition 7 crew member on board the ISS. (Photo: NASA.)

atmosphere falls rapidly with altitude and accordingly the pressure also falls. At an altitude of only 6km it is half its sea-level value. The pressure continues to halve for approximately every 6km increase in altitude, and at an altitude of around 80km, just below the ionosphere, it is only 0.00001 of atmospheric pressure at sea level.

The atmosphere is made up from a variety of gases. Although the natural tendency would be for the denser gases to settle to the lower altitudes, leaving the lighter gases higher up, this does not occur in practice. The reason for this is that the atmospheric winds continually mix the gases and as a result the proportion of each gas remains virtually the same up to altitudes of 80 to 90km. The principal constituents in the atmosphere are nitrogen (78%) and oxygen (21%). The remaining gases form only about 1%. Of these argon (0.9%) has the highest level, followed by carbon dioxide (0.03%) and varying amounts of water vapour dependent upon the humidity level at that time. Other gases that are found include hydrogen, ozone, methane, carbon monoxide, and some of the inert elements including neon, krypton and xenon.

Atmospheric layers

The atmosphere can be divided up in to a variety of layers according to the different properties they exhibit. Unfortunately there is no single set of nomenclature that can be employed because there are several different systems in use by different organisations and interests. The set that is most applicable for propagation studies is the meteorological one given in **Fig 2.2**. From this it can be seen that the main layers are the *troposphere* closest to the Earth. Above this is the *stratosphere*, followed by the *mesosphere*, and finally there is the *thermosphere*. The boundaries between these layers are based on the temperature variations that exist and as a result the exact altitudes of the different areas vary from day to day, and according to their location.

The temperature in the troposphere falls as the altitude increases. It falls to nearly −60°C, typically

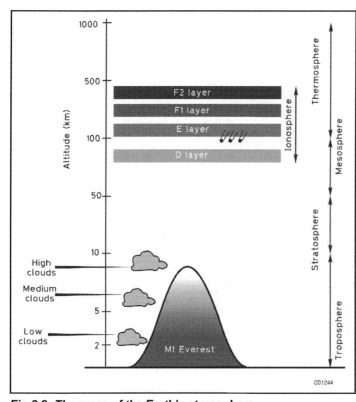

Fig 2.2: The areas of the Earth's atmosphere.

at an altitude of around 10km. It then rises in the stratosphere, almost reaching 0°C at the border with the mesosphere, where again the temperature falls to around −90°C at the border with the thermosphere. Then the temperature rises again, reaching around 1200°C. There are two main areas of the atmosphere that affect radio signals. The first is the *troposphere*, and the second is the *ionosphere* which extends over the mesosphere and thermosphere. These two areas act on radio signals in very different ways but enable them to travel over distances that are greater than just the line of sight.

The troposphere

This is the portion of the atmosphere that is closest to the ground and it is here that most of the conditions that affect the weather occur. Clouds may extend virtually from ground level to the highest ones which may reach as high as 8 or 10km. High- and low-pressure areas also exist, as do winds and the other features that govern the weather conditions.

Another feature of the troposphere that is of importance is that the pressure and temperature fall with increasing altitude. The temperature falls steadily to around −60°C at the *tropopause* – the point at which the temperature starts to rise and the boundary with the stratosphere.

The refractive index of the air in the troposphere plays a major role in radio signal propagation. This is dependent upon a number of factors including the temperature, the pressure and the level of humidity. There are noticeable changes in the values of all three of these measures close to the ground and as a result tropospheric propagation normally occurs at altitudes less than about 3km.

The ionosphere

The ionosphere is an area of the atmosphere that is contained within more than one of the meteorological areas. Encompassed by the mesosphere and the thermosphere, it is an area that is characterised by the existence of positive ions (and, more importantly for radio signals, free electrons), and it is from the existence of the ions that it gains its name.

The number of free electrons starts to rise at altitudes of approximately 30km but it is not until around 80 or 90km are reached that the concentration is sufficiently high to start to have a noticeable effect on radio signals.

In essence the ionisation in the upper atmosphere is caused by radiation from the Sun. However, there are other aspects that need to be considered. In view of the very high temperatures and the low pressure, gases in the upper reaches of the atmosphere exist mainly in a monatomic form rather than molecules. At lower altitudes the gases are in the normal molecular form but, as the altitude increases, the monatomic forms are more in abundance, and at altitudes of around 150km most of the gases are in a monatomic form. This is very important because the monatomic forms of the gases are very much easier to ionise than the molecular ones.

The Sun emits vast quantities of radiation of all wavelengths and this travels towards the Earth, first reaching the outer areas of the atmosphere. Ionisation occurs when radiation of sufficient intensity strikes an atom or a mole-

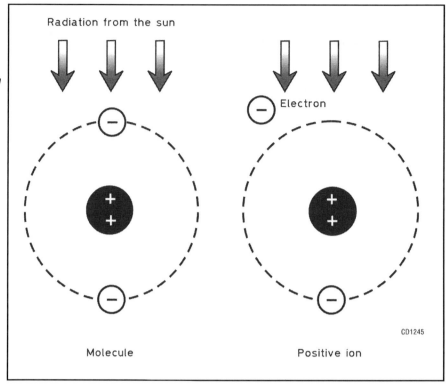

Fig 2.3: Radiation strikes a gas atom to form a positive ion and a free electron.

Radiation from the sun

Electron

Molecule

Positive ion

CD1245

cule – energy may be absorbed from the radiation and an electron detached, producing a free electron and a positive ion. The simple example of a helium atom is given in **Fig 2.3**, although other gases including oxygen and nitrogen are far more common.

The radiation from the Sun appears as a variety of wavelengths but can be considered to be photons. From **Fig 2.3** it can be seen that the electrons are orbiting the central nucleus which consists of protons and neutrons.

Electrons are tied or bound to their orbit around the nucleus by electrostatic forces. The electron is negatively charged and the nucleus is positively charged – since there are equal numbers of electrons and protons in any molecule it is electrostatically neutral. When a photon strikes the atom or molecule, the photon transfers its energy to the electron as excess kinetic energy. Under some circumstances this excess energy may exceed the binding energy in the atom or molecule and the electron escapes the influence of the positive charge of the nucleus. This leaves a positively charged nucleus or *ion* and a negatively charged electron, although as there are the same number of positive ions and negative electrons the whole gas still remains with an overall neutral charge.

Of the radiation that reaches the Earth, most of the ionisation is caused by ultra-violet light, although other wavelengths also play a part in the process. Each time an atom or molecule is ionised a small amount of energy is used. This means that as the radiation passes further into the atmosphere, its intensity reduces. It is for this reason that the ultra-violet radiation causes most of the ionisation in the upper reaches of the ionosphere, but at lower altitudes extreme ultra-violet and X-rays give rise to most of it. This reduction in these forms of radiation protects us on the surface of the Earth from their harmful effects.

Although the radiation is at its most intense at the edge of the atmosphere, the levels of ionisation vary with altitude. There are a number of reasons for this – the density of the gases varies and there is also a variation in the proportions of monatomic and molecular forms of the gases. These and a variety of other phenomena mean that there are variations in the level of ionisation with altitude.

Often the ionosphere is thought of as a number of distinct layers. This is a con-

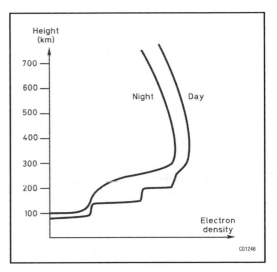

Fig 2.4: The typical electron distribution in the ionosphere.

venient way of picturing its structure but it is not strictly true. There is ionisation over the whole of the ionosphere, and its level varies at different altitudes, rising and falling. The peaks in level may be considered as the different layers or regions. These regions are given letter designations: D, E and F regions. There is in fact a C region beneath the others but the level of ionisation is very low and it does not affect radio signals. Accordingly it is rarely mentioned. It can be seen quite clearly from **Fig 2.4** that the different regions are peaks in the levels of ionisation. This is only a very approximate guide as the levels vary considerably as the result of a number of other factors.

One of the main reasons for the variation of the electron density in the ionosphere changing with time is the fact that the radiation from the Sun is only present during the day. This radiation causes the atoms and molecules to split into free electrons and positive ions but the reverse effect also occurs. When a negative electron meets a positive ion, the fact that dissimilar charges attract means that they will be pulled towards one another and they may combine. This means that two opposite effects of splitting and recombination are taking place. This is known as a *state of dynamic equilibrium*. Accordingly the level of ionisation is dependent upon the rate of ionisation and recombination.

The effect can be likened to a tank of water being filled. If water is drawn off the level of the water in the tank is dependent upon the amount of water being run into it as well as the amount of water being drawn out. Here the water being used to fill the tank is equivalent to the radiation causing ionisation, and the water being drawn out is equivalent to the recombination. The depth of water in the tank is the amount of ionisation. If the Sun sets and the radiation is removed this is like the water supply flowing into the tank being stopped. This will result in the level of water in the tank falling.

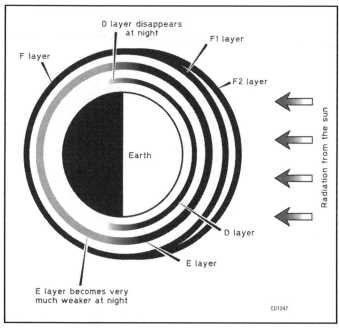

Fig 2.5: A simplified view of the layers in the ionosphere over the period of a day.

Ionospheric regions

The different regions in the ionosphere have many different characteristics in the way they are generated, are sustained and the way they affect radio waves. In view of this it is worth taking a closer look at each one in detail and the way they vary over the complete day during light and darkness (**Fig 2.5**).

The condition of the Sun also has a major effect on the state of the ionosphere. The level of radiation that it emits changes with time and this can have a significant effect on the ionosphere. These changes are investigated in the next chapter.

D region

This region is the lowest one that significantly affects radio signals, existing at altitudes between about 60 and 90km. It is only present to any degree during the day when radiation from the Sun is present, levels of ionisation falling rapidly when the Sun sets. It mainly has the affect of absorbing or attenuating radio signals, particularly in the LF and MF portions of the radio spectrum, its effect reducing with frequency. At night it has little effect on most radio signals, although there is still a sufficient level of ionisation for it to refract VLF signals.

The layer is chiefly generated by the action of a form of radiation known as *Lyman-alpha radiation* which has a wavelength of 1215Å (ångströms: 1Å is equal to 10^{-10}m or 10^{-8}cm) and ionises nitric oxide gas present in the atmosphere. Hard X-rays also contribute to the ionisation, especially towards the peak of the solar cycle.

E region

The region that is found above the D region is obviously known as the *E region*. It exists at altitudes between about 100 and 125km. Instead of attenuating signals this layer chiefly 'reflects' or, more correctly, *refracts* them, although they are still attenuated to some degree.

In this region, like the D region, the level of ionisation falls relatively quickly after dark as the electrons and ions re-combine and it virtually disappears at night. However, the residual night-time ionisation in the lower part of the E region causes some attenuation of signals in the lower portions of the HF part of the radio spectrum.

The ionisation in this region results from a number of types of radiation. Soft X-rays produce much of the ionisation, although extreme ultra-violet (EUV) rays (very-short-wavelength ultra-violet light) also contribute. Broadly the radiation that produces ionisation in this region has wavelengths between about 10 and 100Å. The degree to which all of the constituents contribute depends upon the state of the Sun and the latitude at which the observations are made.

F region

The highest and most important region from the point of view of long-distance HF communications is the F region. During the daytime when radiation is being received from the Sun, it splits into two, the lower one being the F1 region and the higher one the F2 region. Of these the F1 region is more of an inflection point in the electron density curve and it generally only exists in the summer.

The altitude of the layers varies considerably and figures given should only be taken as a rough guide. Being the highest of the ionospheric regions, it is greatly affected by the state of the Sun as well as other factors including the time of day, the year and so forth. Typically the F1 layer is found at around an altitude of 300km with the F2 layer above it at around 400km. The combined F layer may then be centred around 250 to 300km. The F layer acts as a 'reflector' of signals in the HF portion of the spectrum, enabling world-wide communications to be established. It is the main region associated with HF signal propagation.

Like the D and E layers the level of ionisation of this region varies over the course of the day, falling at night as the radiation from the Sun disappears. However, it remains much higher. The density of the gases is much lower, and as a result the recombination of the ions and electrons takes place more slowly, at about a quarter of the rate that it occurs in the E region. Consequently it still has an effect on signals at night, being able to return many to Earth, although it has a reduced effect in some aspects.

As the F region is at the highest altitude, it experiences the full force of the solar radiation, and much of the ionisation results from ultra-violet light in the middle of the spectrum as well as those portions of the spectrum with very short wavelengths. Typically the radiation that causes the ionisation is between the wavelengths of 100 and 1000Å, although extreme ultra-violet light is responsible for some ionisation in the lower areas of the F region. See **Table 2.1**.

Region	Primary ionising radiation forms
C	Cosmic rays
D	Lyman-alpha, hard X-rays
E	Soft X-rays and some extreme ultra-violet
F1	Extreme ultra-violet, some ultra-violet
F2	Ultra-violet

Table 2.1. Summary of forms of radiation causing ionisation in the ionosphere.

Ionospheric variations

It has already been seen that the time of day causes some very significant changes in the state of the ionosphere as the level of ionisation falls at night. However, there are many other factors that have an effect on the ionosphere. The main one is the Sun itself but this will be discussed in the next chapter. Other factors include the season and the position on the globe.

Seasonal changes

In just the same way that the amount of heat places on the Earth receive varies with the seasons, so does the amount of radiation received by the ionosphere. This results from the fact that in summer the radiation spreads over a smaller area as the Earth's surface is closer to being at right-angles to the direction of the radiation. In winter, the surface is at a greater angle and the radiation has to spread over a larger area. Consequently the ionosphere receives less radiation in winter than summer.

The D and E regions respond as expected, with lower levels of ionisation in winter than summer, and the F1 region also follows a similar pattern. However, for the F2 region there are other influencing factors and it responds in a different way.

For the F2 region, the heating effect of the Sun plays a crucial role in the way it responds. The temperature during the winter is much less than in the summer as a result of the heat from the Sun being spread over a larger area because the Sun is lower in the sky. In summer the gas temperature rises in the F2 region so the activity in the air rises and a greater number of molecules rise higher up into the atmosphere.

In winter, as the temperature falls, the heavier molecules fall, leaving the lighter atoms to rise to the top. This means that in winter there is a higher proportion of atoms at the higher altitude of the F2 region. Atoms are easier to ionise than gas molecules, and so the number of suitable targets for the radiation to ionise also rises. As a result the levels of daytime ionisation are actually higher in winter than they are in the summer. The overall effect is that the peak daytime levels of ionisation rise higher in winter than summer, but they fall away to a lower level as the Sun's radiation is present for a smaller proportion of the time.

Geographical variations

The levels of ionisation are also affected by the position on the globe. There are naturally variations arising from the latitude – polar regions receive less radiation and the equatorial regions enjoy much higher levels. Broadly this results in higher levels of ionisation for the D, E and F1 regions in equatorial areas than towards the poles.

The F2 region has a number of other factors that affect its level of ionisation, including the Earth's magnetic field and it also receives ionisation from other sources.

As a result of these the levels of ionisation are higher around Asia and Australia than they are over the western hemisphere, including Africa, Europe, and North America.

Beyond the ionosphere

The Earth's atmosphere reaches up to many hundreds of kilometres. It is generally accepted that the ionosphere extends to altitudes of 600km. Here the density of the gases is so low that the levels of ionisation fall to a point where they have no noticeable affect on radio signals.

Beyond the ionosphere there are still regions associated with the Earth that have an effect on radio signal propagation. The main area of importance is associated with

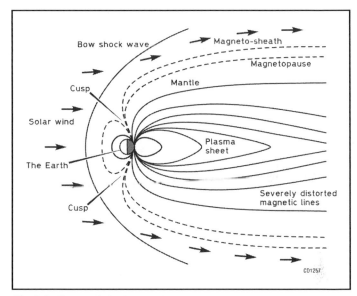

Fig 2.6: Beyond the ionosphere.

the magnetic field that surrounds the Earth. This arises from the movement of the fluids within the core of the Earth and the resulting currents that flow. This gives rise to the magnetic north and south poles. See **Fig 2.6**.

Emanating from the Sun is a steady stream of charged particles in the form of the *solar wind*. As the particles are charged they interact with the Earth's geomagnetic field and a shock wave is set up. This is named the *magneto-sheath*, and the solar wind flows around this. It is at a distance of about 10 Earth radii from the Earth. The action of the solar wind distorts the Earth's magnetic or geomagnetic field, creating a long tail extending away from the Sun. Thus the magnetic field is compressed on the day side of the Earth, and drawn out on the night side. The geomagnetic field protects the Earth from the solar wind, which does not enter the area within the magnetosheath – this region is called the *magnetosphere*.

Within the magnetosphere there are areas where charged particles from the solar wind become trapped by the geomagnetic lines of force. They travel at very large velocities and oscillate back and forth in what are named the Van Allen belts, after their discoverer. Currently much is unknown about these belts and more work is needed before there is a complete understanding of the way the particles from the solar wind become trapped.

What is known is that during periods of high solar activity, when the solar wind greatly increases, it causes electrons trapped in the Van Allen belts in the magnetosphere to enter the Earth's atmosphere at both poles, creating the auroras, ie the Northern and Southern Lights. These can only be seen towards the poles but they are dramatic and quite beautiful, appearing as slowly changing lights in the sky.

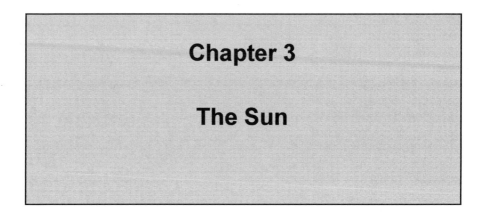

Chapter 3

The Sun

The Sun is the central point of the Solar System. It is the sole provider of energy that enables life on Earth to exist, and it is also the source of radiation that gives rise to the ionosphere. Upon it depends the state of the ionosphere and hence it is of great interest to anyone concerned with ionospheric radio propagation.

The Sun has inspired stories, myths and religions since the very earliest times. This is not surprising since it dominates the daytime skies. It is a sphere of mostly ionised gas and is about 4.5 billion years old. The Earth is about 150 million kilometres away from the Sun, and even at this distance it supplies an energy level of about 1.36kW/m2.

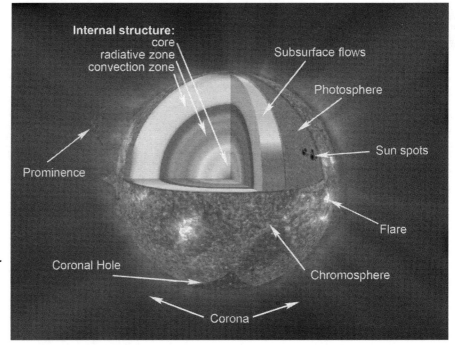

Fig 3.1: A representation of the regions in the Sun. (Image: NASA.)

Overall the Sun is composed of 90% hydrogen, 9% helium, and the remaining 1% is made up from heavier trace elements.

Solar interior

The Sun is around 333,400 times more massive than the Earth and contains over 99.85% of the mass of the whole Solar System. This has prompted one comment that the solar system consists of a star and some debris. Although fundamentally a gaseous body, the Sun is held together by tremendous gravitational forces that reach colossal values at its centre.

The internal regions of the Sun have a complex structure but it has still been possible for solar scientists to gain a good understanding of some of the processes that occur. Research is ongoing all the time and, with the new techniques being employed, the understanding of all the areas of the Sun is continually growing. Nevertheless, there are still many regions that are not fully understood, although it has been possible to deduce that there are a number of different areas where the various processes occur. **Fig 3.1** shows the internal make-up of the Sun as well as some of the features on its surface.

First there is a central core where the energy is generated. Once generated, energy moves outwards by radiation and convection through what is termed the *radiative zone* and through a thin interface called the *tachocline* to the convection zone. Beyond these are the *photosphere, chromosphere* and the *corona*.

The core

The Sun's core is the central region where the energy is generated and it forms the inner 25% of the radius of the Sun. The energy is produced as nuclear reactions convert hydrogen to helium and the amounts are colossal, with over 383 billion trillion watts of energy generated, equivalent to 100 billion tons of TNT being exploded every second. This results in temperatures in this region reaching around 15,000,000°C and, as a result of the enormous gravitational fields, the density of this region reaches about 150g/cm^3 which is about 10 times that of lead.

The nuclear activity decreases towards the edge of the core which is about 175,000km from the very centre. Here too the temperature has fallen to around half the maximum value at the centre and the density is only about 20g/cm^3.

The radiative zone

This region extends outwards from the core from a distance equivalent to 25% of the radius of the Sun to about 70%. Here energy is transferred outwards primarily by radiation. Although the energy travels at the speed of light it bounces around in this area and it is estimated that it takes about a million years for the energy to reach the *interface zone* or *tachocline*.

As the gravitational forces are considerably less in this region the density falls from around 20g/cm^3 to around 0.2g/cm^3 which actually less than that of water. Also the temperature falls from around 7,000,000°C to around 2,000,000°C.

The tachocline

This layer is also known as the *interface zone* as it acts as an interface between the radiative zone and the convection zone. The two layers transfer energy in very different ways, and the fluid motion of the convection zone above the tachocline disappears to match the more stable material conditions of the radiative zone.

The other important feature of this zone is that it is now thought that the Sun's magnetic field is generated here. It is believed that shearing flows across the layer can stretch the magnetic lines of force and enhance them. In addition to this, there appear to be sudden changes in the chemical composition across the layer.

The convection zone

This is the outermost layer of the interior region of the Sun. The temperature across the tachocline remains almost constant and therefore the temperature at the inner areas of the convection zone is around 2,000,000°C.

This falls to around 5700°C at the visible surface of the convection zone. These falling temperatures result in many of the heavier ions such as carbon, nitrogen and oxygen retaining their electrons. As a result the material becomes opaque and this makes it more difficult for the heat to be transferred. Consequently the layer starts to 'boil' and then movement occurs as convection takes place.

2003/10/28 06:24 UT

Fig 3.2. A view of the photosphere. Note that it is darker towards the edge and lighter in the middle where, looking directly at the Sun it is possible to see deeper in to the hotter regions. Also note the sunspots. Image taken by the Solar and Heliospheric Observatory. (Image: NASA / SOHO.)

Photosphere

It is the photosphere that forms the visible surface of the Sun. This region or layer is not a solid surface and is actually only about 100km thick. Also, being gaseous, it is possible to see through it when looking at the centre of the Sun with the right equipment and it is for this reason that images of the Sun look darker around the edges than in the centre, where the hotter deeper regions are viewed. This phenomenon can be seen in **Fig 3.2**.

Warning: The Sun is exceedingly bright and should never be viewed directly, even with dark glasses, as many people have been blinded by doing this.

When viewing the surface of the Sun it is possible to see a number of features, including the *granules* and *supergranules* at the surface of the convection zone (**Figs 3.3** and **3.4**).

These granules are the result of the motion within the convection zone where the denser, lower-temperature, material moves around as hotter material moves to the surface as a result of convection.

Fig 3.3: Granules on the surface of the Sun, 24 July 2002. (Image: Professor Göran Scharmer / Dr Mats G Löfdahl, Royal Swedish Academy of Sciences.)

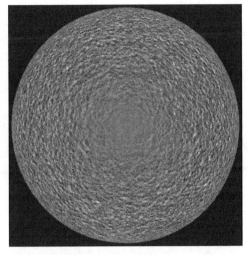

Fig 3.4: The enormous supergranules can be seen relative to the whole surface of the Sun. (Image: NASA / SOHO.)

The chromosphere

This is an irregular layer that exists above the photosphere. In this region hydrogen emits a reddish light as a result of an increase in temperature to around 20,000°C.

Corona

The Sun's corona can be found beyond the chromosphere. It is effectively the Sun's outer atmosphere and can be seen during eclipses as an area surrounding the Sun (**Fig 3.5**). Within the corona, gases become heated to

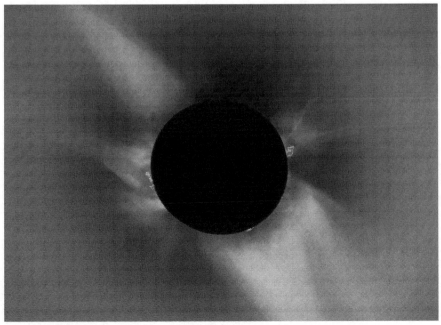

Fig 3.5. An image of the solar corona with streamers and plumes extending into space. (Image: NASA).

31

a temperature of around 1,000,000°C, and at these temperatures the dominant elements of hydrogen and helium atoms become completely stripped of their electrons. Other elements, including carbon, nitrogen and oxygen, fare similarly although calcium, being much heavier, does manage to retain its electrons.

These highly ionised elements generate light emissions with well-defined spectral lines. For many years astronomers had wondered where and how they were created. It was only the development of new equipment that enabled the true origin to be discovered.

In view of the large temperature difference between the chromosphere and the corona there is a sharp transition region. This separates the very hot corona at around 1,000,000°C from the chromosphere at around 20,000°C.

Sun's rotation

The Sun rotates on its axis and has a rotation period normally taken to be about 27 days. However, as the Sun is a gaseous body it does not all rotate at the same speed. The equatorial regions are faster, taking about 24 days to complete a revolution, whereas the polar regions take over 30 days. The rotation speeds and times can be judged by monitoring the sunspots and other features that may appear on the surface.

Additionally the axis of rotation of the Sun is tilted at an angle of 7.25° to the axis of the Earth's orbit, and this means that more of the solar north pole is seen in September and its south pole in March.

Sunspots

A feature of the Sun that is of great important to radio signal propagation is the dark spots – *sunspots* – that appear on its surface (**Fig 3.6**). They play a major role in determining the state of the ionosphere because associated

Fig 3.6: Sunspots on the surface of the Sun. (Image: NASA.)

with them is an increase in the level of solar radiation.

The spots have been observed for many years. It is known that the ancient Chinese civilisation observed them many years prior to the birth of Christ. However, it was not until the early 17th century after Galileo had invented the telescope that he was able to observe them more closely by projecting an image on to a piece of paper – several of his original sketches are still in existence today (**Fig 3.7**).

It was not until the middle of the 18th century that records of sunspot numbers were kept on a regular basis and, as the numbers varied significantly and apparently in a random fashion, it took some years before the sunspot cycle was noticed. After observing the Sun for almost 20 years and mathematically analysing the result, a

Fig 3.7: Galileo's drawing of sunspots observed on 26 June 1613.

scientist named Schwabe discovered the cyclical variation of the sunspots, publishing his findings in 1843. Today further research has revealed many more details about these spots, but there is still plenty that scientists are keen to discover.

Sunspots are transitory and may last for anywhere from a few days to a few weeks or even months. They appear dark, as the temperature on their surface is only about 3700°C compared with the remainder of the photosphere that is at around 5700°C.

Sunspots are first seen as a very small dark spot called a *pore*. Not all these pores develop into full spots, but the ones that do steadily develop over a period of hours or days to become full spots. As it becomes larger a lighter area is seen around the dark spot. The dark spot itself is referred to as the *umbra* and the lighter area around it is the *penumbra*.

Sunspots often appear in clusters. Each spot can be anywhere from a few hundred miles in diameter to almost 100,000 miles across. The groups themselves can contain several large spots and may be over a quarter of a million miles in diameter.

The spots arise from very intense magnetic fields that exist below the surface of the Sun. These fields change during the course of the cycle. At the sunspot minimum the magnetic fields are longitudinal, running from the Sun's north to its south. As the Sun rotates the fields rotate at a different speed, the equatorial regions spinning more slowly than the poles. This causes distortion of the fields that slowly align in an east-west direction. As a result of these changes the activity on the Sun varies in a cyclical form, having a distinct trough and peak.

At times the changes in the magnetic fields cause eruptions to take place through the Sun's surface. Around the eruptions the surface temperature falls dramatically, giving rise to what are seen as dark spots.

The area around the spot has a large temperature differential, and there is also a large disturbance in the magnetic field. The magnetic fields are unusually strong, with strengths many thousands of times that of the Earth's, and this results in enormous forces being produced. When a group of spots appear, one cluster will have a positive, or northerly, magnetic field and the other has a negative or southerly magnetic field. The field is the strongest in the darker part of the spot and weakest in the lighter part.

Large levels of electromagnetic energy and cosmic rays emanate from around the spots and this affects the levels of ionisation in the ionosphere.

Sunspot numbers

As can be imagined, different astronomers with different equipment will arrive at different numbers of sunspots. Shortly after the discovery of sunspots Rudolf Wolf, who was the director of the Zurich observatory, devised a system giving the relative sunspot activity. This could then be used as a common standard for all observatories. The activity is defined in terms of a *sunspot number*, which is not the actual number of sunspots which are seen.

$$R = k(10g + s)$$

where R is the Wolf number for sunspot activity, k is a correction factor to take account of the equipment and observer characteristics, g is the number of sunspot groups and s is the number of observable spots (whether individually or in groups).

This formula weights the sunspot activity number heavily towards clusters. This may appear to be incorrect, but Wolf chose to adopt this system because he deduced that the large clusters were a better indication of sunspot activity than short-lived spots on their own. Despite its shortcomings, it is still a very useful indicator because sunspot numbers have been measured in this way for over 200 years and it gives very useful comparisons and visibility of trends over the whole period.

The day-to-day numbers of sunspot activity vary widely. In order to view the trends the data are averaged or smoothed over a wider period. Two stages are used for this. First the daily numbers are averaged over the period of a month and then the monthly figures are smoothed over a 12-month period. In order to ensure that the mean falls right in the middle of the month in question, rather than between months, the period of smoothing is run over 13 months, but taking half the value for the months at either end:

$$R_s = \frac{0.5R_{m1} + R_{m2} + R_{m3} + \ldots R_{m11} + R_{m12} + 0.5R_{m13}}{12}$$

where R_s is the smoothed sunspot number and R_{m1} to R_{m13} are the monthly averaged numbers for months 1 to 13.

Both the monthly average sunspot numbers and the smoothed values are available for use in propagation predictions, although the smoothed figures are much in arrears. The numbers are now prepared by the Solar Influences Data Analysis Center (SIDC) in Brussels from information supplied by a number of observatories. They appear in DX propagation information available from a wide variety of sources including the RSGB. The 12-month smoothed sunspot number correlates quite closely with the prevailing HF radio propagation conditions.

Sunspot cycle

Once the numbers were smoothed a trend was detected and it could be seen that there was cyclical variation with a period of about 11 years. These cycles are now given numbers starting with cycle 1 which began in 1755. Since then there have been over 20 more cycles and at the time of writing in 2016 we are currently in the declining phase of solar cycle 24 (**Fig 3.8**).

A number of factors have become obvious from analysis of the figures since the first records were available. The first is that the cycles are by no means very regular. Although the average cycle length when measured as the time between two peaks is about 10.9 years, it varies anywhere from just over seven years to 17 years. The smoothed sunspot numbers also vary widely. The maximum sunspot activity numbers vary from 49 to 200 with an average of just over 100. The minimum number can be anywhere between zero and 12.

Usually after the sunspot minimum sunspot activity rises sharply, reaching the peak in around four years, and after this it falls away more slowly, taking around seven years to decay. Naturally this figure too varies very widely and it can only be taken as a very rough guide.

The sunspot cycle is of great interest to anyone using the HF portion of the radio spectrum. Propagation conditions are greatly influenced by sunspot activity, and accordingly they vary

Fig 3.8: The sunspot cycle since records began, updated 1 August 2016. (Image: SILSO, Royal Observatory of Belgium, Brussels.)

in line with the sunspot cycle. At the low point of the cycle, the high-frequency bands above 20MHz or so may not support ionospheric reflections, whereas at the peak of the cycle frequencies at 50MHz and higher may be reflected.

Ionospheric indicators

The number of sunspots which are seen at any time gives a guide to the amount of radiation being received by the ionosphere. Although the sunspot number can be calculated, a more objective method of achieving this is to look at the amount of radiation coming from the Sun. Not only does the Sun emit vast quantities of heat and light, it also emits energy at radio frequencies. An indication of solar activity can be made by measuring the level of solar noise. This is normally taken at a frequency of 2800MHz (a wavelength of 10.7cm) and is called the *solar flux*. It has been shown that it follows the daily sunspot number and a number of relationships have been devised. One of the most straightforward is that:

$$\text{Solar flux} = 73.4 + 0.62R$$

where R is the daily sunspot count.

Solar wind

There is a constant stream of material that emanates from the Sun. This *solar wind* streams off it in all directions at speeds of up to 400km a second (about a million miles an hour). The actual source of the wind is the corona where the temperature is so high that the gravitational forces of the Sun are overcome and the material escapes. The exact method by which the material is accelerated to such colossal velocities is not yet understood. The level of the wind is affected by a number of factors and is increased in some directions when there are solar disturbances.

The solar wind reaches the Earth and, as mentioned in the previous chapter, it is deflected around the Earth by its magnetic field under most circumstances. However, under conditions where there are solar disturbances this can create geomagnetic and ionospheric storms on Earth.

Solar disturbances

With such enormous levels of energy and high temperatures, it is hardly surprising that there are periodic disturbances on the Sun. These disturbances can be of truly enormous proportions, with vast quantities of material being flung out into the solar system along with tremendous increases in the level of radiation being emitted. This can have a serious effect on the Earth, resulting in major changes in radio propagation conditions along with other effects such as auroras, the Northern and Southern Lights.

Flares

Solar flares are enormous explosions that occur on the surface of the Sun. When they occur they radiate huge amounts of energy, and larger events also eject large amounts of material mainly in the form of protons into outer space (**Fig 3.9**). They erupt in a matter of just a few minutes, heating material to millions of degrees kelvin and ejecting colossal amounts of it from the surface of the Sun. They occur near sunspots, usually along the dividing or neutral line between areas of oppositely directed magnetic fields.

The key to understanding and predicting solar flares is the structure of the magnetic field around sunspots. When this structure becomes twisted and sheared magnetic field lines can cross and reconnect with an explosive release of energy. When this occurs an eruption of gases takes place through the solar surface, and it extends several tens of thousands of miles from the surface of

Fig 3.9: A solar flare. (Image: NASA Solar Dynamics Observatory.)

the Sun. The gases from within the Sun start to rise and the area becomes heated even more – this causes the level of visible radiation and other forms of radiation to increase. Although the actual mechanism is not fully understood, material may break through the surface of the Sun, following the magnetic lines of force.

Initially high-velocity protons travelling at around a third the speed of light are ejected, then after about five minutes lower-energy particles follow. This material follows the arc of the magnetic lines of force and returns to the Sun, although some material is ejected into outer space especially during the larger flares.

For most flares it is mainly the increase in radiation that affects the Earth. This radiation covers the electromagnetic spectrum and includes ultra-violet, X-rays and cosmic rays as well as radio-frequency emissions. In fact the radio-frequency radiation can be heard distinctly on the VHF bands as an increase in the level of background noise.

Flares generally only last for about an hour, after which the surface of the Sun returns to normal, although some post-flare loops remain for a while afterwards. The flares affect radio propagation on Earth and the effects may be noticed for some time afterwards.

Flares are classified by their intensity at X-ray wavelengths (1 – 8Å). The X-ray intensity from the Sun is continually monitored by the National Oceanic and Atmospheric Administration (NOAA) using detectors on some of its satellites. Using this data it is possible to classify the flares. The largest flares are termed *X-class flares*. M-class flares are smaller, having a tenth the X-ray intensity of the X-class ones. C-class flares have a tenth the intensity of the M-class ones.

In view of the fact that flares are associated with sunspots, their occurrence correlates well with the sunspot cycle. Accordingly there are significantly more around the peak of the sunspot cycle.

CMEs

Another form of disturbance that takes place on the Sun is known as a *coronal mass ejection* (CME), **Fig 3.10**. These disturbances are huge bubbles of gas that are threaded with magnetic field lines, and the bubbles are ejected over the space of several hours. For many years it was thought that solar flares were responsible for ejecting the masses of particles that gave rise to the auroral disturbances that are experienced on Earth. Now it is understood that CMEs are the primary cause.

CMEs can only be observed by looking at the corona around the Sun. Prior to the space age this could only be done during an eclipse. As these occur relatively infrequently, and only last for a few minutes, CMEs were not seen until spacecraft could monitor the Sun from space. Using a *coronagraph*, a specialised telescope with what is termed an *occulting disk*, enabling it to cut out the main area of the Sun and only view the corona, it was possible to observe the activity in the coronal area. This enabled CMEs to be discovered and then monitored. Although ground-based coronagraphs are available, they are only able to view the very bright innermost area of the corona. Space-based ones are able to gain a very much better view of the corona, extending to very large distances from the Sun, and in this way see far more of the activity in this region.

It is now understood that CMEs disrupt the steady flow of the solar wind, producing a large increase in the flow. This may result in large disturbances that might strike the Earth if they leave the Sun in the right direction.

CMEs are often associated with solar flare eruptions but they can also occur on their own. Like solar flares their frequency varies according to the position in the sunspot cycle, peaking around the sunspot maximum and falling around the minimum. At solar minimum there may be about one each week while at the peak two or three may be observed each day. Fortunately they do not all affect the Earth. Material is thrown out from the Sun in one general direction and only if this is on an intersecting trajectory will it affect the Earth.

The plasma within a CME carries within it a 'frozen-in' magnetic field that interacts with the Earth's magnetic field. If the magnetic field of the plasma (Bz) is pointing North, the cloud bounces off it fairly harmlessly, like similar poles of small bar magnets.

But in the opposite field direction (Bz pointing south) the field lines of the plasma are said to 'connect' with the geomagnetic field, just like a bar magnet's opposite poles. This situation opens up cracks in the Earth's defences and charged particles flood in to cause auroras and geomagnetic storms.

Fig 3.10: Coronal mass ejection, 1 January 2013. (Image: JPL / NASA SDO.)

Coronal holes

Coronal holes are another important feature of solar activity (**Fig 3.11**). They are regions where the corona appears dark when viewed in extreme UV or X-ray images. They were first discovered after X-ray telescopes were first launched into space and, being above the Earth's atmosphere, they were able to study the structure of the corona across the solar disc. Coronal holes are associated with 'open' magnetic field lines and are often, although not exclusively, found at the Sun's poles. The high-speed solar wind is known to originate from them and this has an impact on ionospheric radio propagation conditions.

Fig 3.11 The dark area of the coronal hole can be seen on the right of the Sun. (Image: NASA.)

In the following chapters it will be seen how the Sun affects the ionosphere, and how this enables radio signals to propagate around the Earth. However, the state of the Sun is of particular interest because it governs the level of ionisation and the overall state of the ionosphere, and hence ionospheric radio propagation conditions.

Chapter 4

Propagation near the ground

One form of radio wave propagation that is widely used on the LF and MF portions of the spectrum is the *ground wave*. It is ideal for relatively short-distance propagation on these frequencies and is used by broadcast stations on the long and medium wavebands to achieve their coverage during the daytime. Sky-wave ionospheric propagation on these frequencies is not possible during the day due to the attenuation of the signals caused by the D region in the ionosphere. In view of this, stations need to rely on ground-wave propagation to achieve their coverage.

A ground-wave signal is made up from a variety of constituents. If the antennas are in the line of sight there will be a direct wave as well as a reflected signal. In addition to this there is a *surface wave*. This tends to follow the curvature of the Earth and enables coverage to be achieved beyond the horizon. It is the sum of all these components that is known as the 'ground wave'.

Beyond the horizon the direct and reflected waves are blocked by the curvature of the Earth and the signal is purely made up from the diffracted surface wave. This why propagation via the surface wave is commonly called 'ground-wave propagation.

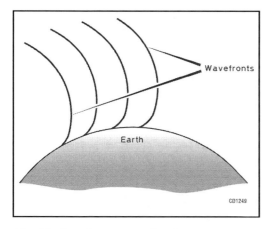

Fig 4.1: A surface wave signal.

Surface wave

The signal spreads out from the transmitter along the surface of the Earth. Instead of just travelling in a straight line the signals tend to follow its curvature. This is because currents are induced in the surface of the Earth and this action slows down the wavefront in this region, causing it to tilt downwards towards the Earth as shown in **Fig 4.1**. With the wavefront tilted in this direction it is able to curve around the Earth and be received well beyond the horizon.

The degree of attenuation of the surface wave signal is dependent upon a variety of factors. Frequency is one of the major determining factors as losses rise with increasing frequency. As a result it makes this form of propagation impracticable above the bottom end of the HF portion of the spectrum (3MHz). Typically a signal at 3.0MHz will suffer an attenuation that may be in the region of 20 to 60dB more than one at 0.5MHz dependent upon a variety of factors in the signal path, including the distance. In view of this it can be seen why high-power HF broadcast stations may only be audible for a few miles from the transmitting site via the ground wave.

The surface wave is also very dependent upon the nature of the ground over which the signal travels. Ground conductivity, terrain roughness and the dielectric constant all affect the signal attenuation. In addition to this the ground penetration varies, becoming greater at lower frequencies, and this means that it is not just the surface conductivity that is of interest.

At the higher frequencies this is not of great importance, but at lower ones penetration means that ground strata down to 100m may have an effect.

Despite all these variables, terrain with good conductivity gives the best results. Thus soil type and its moisture content are of importance. Salty sea water is the best, and rich agricultural or marshy land is also good. Dry sandy terrain and city centres are by far the worst. This means sea paths are optimum, although even these are subject to variations due to the roughness of the sea, resulting on path losses being slightly dependent upon the weather! It should also be noted that in view of the fact that signal penetration has an effect, the water table may have an effect dependent upon the frequency in use.

The type of antenna has a major significance. Vertically polarised signals are subject to considerably less attenuation than horizontally polarised ones. In some cases the difference can amount to several tens of decibels. It is for this reason that medium-wave broadcast stations use vertical antennas (**Fig 4.2**), even if they have to be made physically short by adding inductive loading. Ships that used to make use of the MF marine bands often used inverted-L antennas as these are able to to radiate a significant proportion of the signal that is vertically polarised.

Some sky-wave signals may also be present at distances that are typically towards the edge of the ground-wave coverage area, especially at night when the D layer attenuation is reduced. This may serve to reinforce or cancel the overall signal, resulting in figures that will differ from those that may be expected.

Fig 4.2: A medium-wave broadcast antenna: TWR Bonaire, Caribbean, 800kHz. (Image: PJ4DX.)

Chapter 5

Ionospheric propagation

S ignals that are radiated from an antenna travel out in a variety of directions, and some will travel upwards towards the ionosphere. Unlike the ground wave that travels along the ground, the signals that travel upwards towards the ionosphere are termed sky waves, for obvious reasons. Generally sky waves below frequencies of around 20 to 30MHz are 'reflected' by the ionosphere and returned to Earth, and hence signals may be heard from around the globe.

The ionosphere has been used to provide global communications since shortly after the beginnings of radio. Marconi's first transatlantic transmission in 1901 used very low frequencies and forms of ionospheric propagation. Then in the 'twenties the possibilities of using the short-wave (HF) bands started to be investigated and exploited. Radio amateurs made the first transatlantic contact in 1923, and then in 1925 the first trans-globe contacts were made from the UK to New Zealand. Alongside these experiments commercial interests, and in particular the Marconi Company, were investigating the possibility of using these frequencies for long-distance communications. The short-wave bands were used increasingly for all forms of applications from broadcasting to professional communications, and of course they were also widely used by radio amateurs.

Today, it is also possible to use satellites to achieve world-wide communication. They provide a more reliable form of communication because they are not subject to the changes and variations of the ionosphere but they are considerably more expensive to install and maintain, and additionally equipment may not always be available. This means that the short-wave bands combined with ionospheric propagation still have a major role to play in today's communications for professionals and amateurs alike.

Ionospheric layers

The different regions of the ionosphere and their formation have already been described in Chapter 2. Each of these regions, namely the D, E, and F regions, act on radio signals in different ways, attenuating and refracting them. The C region has such a low free electron density that it has no effect on radio signals and will not be discussed further.

D region

The D region (**Fig 5.1**) is the closest ionised region to the surface of the Earth that has an effect on radio signals. In view of this it is the first region that a terrestrial signal encounters on its passage to the ionosphere. It primarily acts as an attenuator to signals in the MF and HF portions of the radio spectrum. In the case of signals in the VLF portion of the radio spectrum, it does not act primarily as an attenuator but instead the same way as the E and F regions, where signals are reflected, or more correctly refracted, back to Earth in a manner described later.

The signal attenuation occurs because the radio signals cause the free electrons in the D region to vibrate in synchronism with the frequency of the signal. As they vibrate they collide with gas molecules around them. At each collision, a small amount of energy is released and this is lost from the signal itself. Accordingly it can be seen that the level of attenuation is proportional to the number of collisions that take place. In turn this is dependent upon a number of other factors.

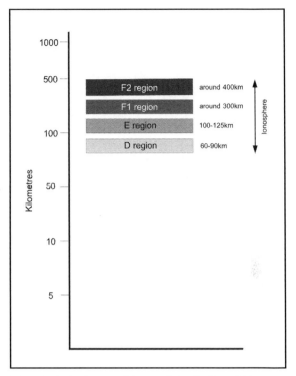

Fig 5.1: Relative positions of the D, E and F regions in the ionosphere.

The first is the number of gas atoms and molecules that are present. The air density at the altitude of the D region is still high when compared to other regions in the ionosphere. As a result a relatively high number of collisions occur. A second factor is the level of ionisation. The C region, for example, has a very much lower level of ionisation, and as a result the effect it has is minimal despite the higher air density in this region.

Finally the frequency has a major bearing. As it increases so the displacement of the electron vibrations decreases, and with this the number of collisions falls. This means that a greater number of collisions occur at low frequencies when the displacement caused by the radio signal is greater. Even so, high-frequency signals still suffer some attenuation. The actual level of attenuation falls as an inverse square law, ie doubling the frequency reduces the level of attenuation by a factor of four.

Mathematically these points can be summarised by stating that the attenuation is proportional to the electron density times the electron / neutral (molecule or atom) collision frequency.

In practical terms, the level of attenuation is sufficient to prevent signals in the MF portion of the spectrum from reaching the higher layers. However, at night when the ionisation in the D region falls away, they are able to reach the higher layers and signals from further away may be heard. This is evident on the medium-wave band and higher frequencies where the signals are absorbed by the D region.

E region

Signals that enter the E region are affected in a somewhat different manner. As before, signals excite the free electrons into vibration but the density of the air is very much reduced and the number of collisions that occur is significantly less. As a result a different effect is noticed. Rather than the electrons colliding with neutrals and dissipating energy they tend to re-radiate the signal. However, as the signal moves to an area of a different electron concentration its direction is changed in much the same way that occurs when a signal passes through an area of changing refractive index. In fact the direction of the signal is refracted away from the area of the higher electron density.

The degree of refraction is often sufficient to enable the signal to be returned to Earth, and in this case the signal is often considered to have been reflected. The degree of refraction is dependent upon a number of factors. One major factor is the degree of ionisation – the greater the level of ionisation, the greater the effect. It is also frequency dependent and higher frequencies are affected less. As the frequency increases, so the signal penetrates further into the layer until it is eventually able to pass through.

It is also found that the angle of incidence is important. Signals that have a low angle of incidence to the ionosphere only require a small degree of refraction to be returned to Earth. Those with a much higher angle of incidence need a much greater degree of refraction. As a result signals with a high angle of incidence enter further into a particular region or layer before being refracted back to Earth, and may even pass straight through (**Fig 5.2**).

Although the major effect of the E region is to reflect signals, the air density, particularly in the lower reaches, is sufficiently high for a significant num-

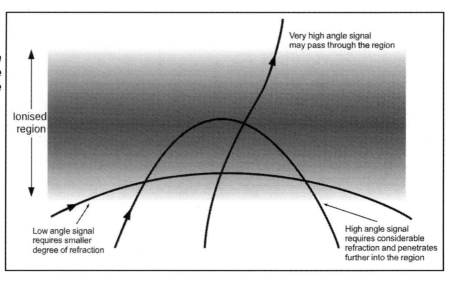

Fig 5.2: Signals with a high angle of incidence require a greater degree of refraction and enter further into the ionised region. They may even pass straight through.

ber of collisions between free electrons and neutrals to occur. As a result there is still some attenuation experienced.

Typically at night when the E region ionisation is low this can result in figures of around 10dB per reflection for signals at around 2MHz.

F1 region

The F1 region occurs above the E region. It acts as a reflector of signals and, as the air density is very low at its altitude, the level of attenuation is small, unlike in the lower areas of the E region. Rather than being a distinct region that sees a maximum electron density that falls off above and below it, the F1 region appears as more of a 'ledge' or inflection point and is often referred to as such.

In terms of propagation it is less important than the F2 region that exists above it.

F2 region

The F2 region is the most prominent ionised region in the atmosphere, as well as being the most important one for long-distance communications. This arises for two reasons. The level of ionisation is by far the greatest of the regions in the ionosphere, and secondly it is the highest in altitude. Having the highest electron density means that it is able to return signals that are higher in frequency to Earth, and also having the highest altitude means that distances that can be achieved are greater.

The region is also characterised by large irregularities. It is therefore not possible to analyse it on a small scale with distances of less than a few kilometres. Even on the large or global scale it presents difficulties to those trying to make forecasts of conditions. The variabilities are not all accounted for by the solar and geomagnetic changes. It possesses a 'climate' of its own, and the changes that occur also influence the way it affects radio signals. These changes make predictions for radio propagation conditions difficult but they are still made and are valuable as statistical indications of the likelihood of the conditions.

Frequency dependence of propagation

The way in which the ionospheric regions respond to signals depends on a variety of factors. One of the major factors is the frequency of the incident signal, so a careful choice of frequency or band is required to enable the required communications to be established. In order to see how the ionosphere reacts to signals at differing frequencies it is useful to consider a signal first at the bottom end of the spectrum and see the changes as the frequency is gradually increased. However, any analysis of this form should only be seen as a very rough guide because the nature of the ionosphere is constantly changing. It is dependent on many factors, including the time of day, the season and the state of the Sun, including the position in the solar sunspot cycle.

Take a signal in the MF portion of the radio spectrum. Typically this might be a medium-wave broadcast transmission. During the daytime this will be

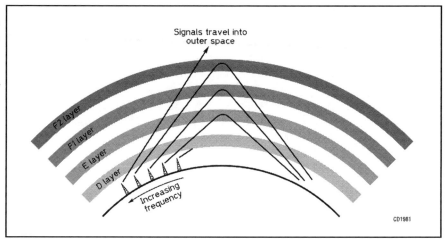

Fig 5.3: Ionospheric signal propagation at different frequencies.

absorbed by the D region and no detectable levels of signal are able to reach the higher regions of the ionosphere and be returned to Earth. At night, as the level of ionisation in the D region disappears, the signals are able to reach the very much reduced E region or the F region and be reflected back to Earth. Although the signals still undergo some attenuation by the lower reaches of the E region they are audible, and this is why interference levels on the medium-wave band increase dramatically at night as stations from further afield can be heard.

As the signal frequency is increased during the day, the level of attenuation introduced by the D region starts to fall. Typically around frequencies just above 2 – 3MHz signals start to penetrate the D region and reach the E region where they are reflected back to Earth (see **Fig 5.3**). They will be audible at much greater distances than are possible via the ground wave. It should be noted that signals are attenuated during each passage through the D region.

As the frequency is increased further the level of attenuation introduced by the D region falls, and signal strengths start to rise. Additionally the signals will penetrate further into the E region and finally they will pass through, reaching the F1 region. Here again they will be reflected back to Earth, and then as the frequency rises still further they will reach the F2 region.

Eventually a point is reached where the signal has such a frequency that none of the layers is able to reflect it and return it to Earth. At this point, and at higher frequencies, it will pass through all the regions of the ionosphere and on into outer space.

Angle of incidence and distances achievable

The angle at which a signal reaches the ionosphere is of great importance. Signals reaching the ionospheric region almost parallel to the contours will need little refraction to return them to Earth. Those reaching the regions with almost vertical incidence will require a much greater degree of refraction. Signals that are attenuated by the D region achieve a lower degree of attenuation if the path length within the D region is as short as possible

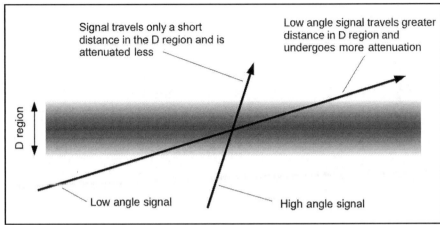

Fig 5.4: Signals that are subject to attenuation receive a lower level of attenuation if they travel in the D region for as short a path as possible.

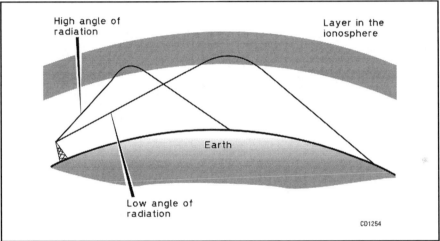

Fig 5.5: Effect of angle of radiation and ionospheric regions on the distances achieved using ionospheric propagation.

(**Fig 5.4**). This means that signals entering the D region almost parallel to it will be attenuated more than those that enter with an angle nearer to the vertical. The distances that can be achieved are also dependent upon the angles at which the signals travel. From basic trigonometry it can be seen that if a signal leaves the antenna at a low angle of radiation, ie almost parallel to the Earth's surface, the distances achieved will be greater than signals leaving with a high angle of radiation, ie travelling at a much steeper angle upwards towards the ionosphere. Also, the higher the ionospheric region that is used, the greater the distances that will be achieved. See **Fig 5.5**.

Even relatively small increases in the angle at which the signal leaves the antenna can considerably reduce the distances that can be covered. The maximum distance that can be achieved using the E layer is generally considered to be 2000km (1250 miles), but this is reduced to just 400km (250 miles) if the angle is 20°. Similarly the maximum distance achievable using the F2 layer reduces from around 4000km (2500 miles) to just under 1000km (600 miles).

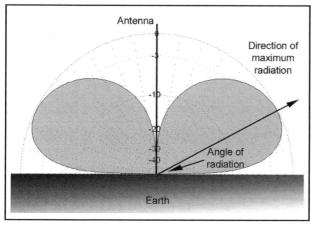

Fig 5.6: Polar diagram plot for a typical vertical antenna.

In order to be able to place the maximum amount of energy where it is required, it is necessary to have a directional antenna. All antennas radiate more energy in some directions than others, and their radiation pattern can be plotted out in a *polar diagram* (**Fig 5.6**). To ensure the optimum performance, the antenna should be orientated in the correct direction and it should have the correct angle of radiation. In many applications where the maximum distance is required, an antenna with a low angle of radiation is needed although, particularly for low frequencies that may be affected by the D region attenuation, this means that it travels through this region for longer and will suffer greater levels of loss. Not all applications require a low angle of radiation. Broadcast stations in particular will arrange for their antennas to have the correct angle of radiation so that the signal has the optimum elevation to reach the required target area.

Skip distance and skip zone

When signals travel from a transmitter to the ionosphere and are reflected back to Earth where they can be heard, the distance from the transmitter to the receiver is known as the *skip distance*, ie the distance that the signal has 'skipped'. There is also an area where it is not possible to hear the signal. This arises because the sky-wave signal may not be reflected back to Earth until some distance away from the transmitter. This can happen because signals travelling upwards at a high angle towards the ionosphere may pass straight through. As a result only those signals at lower angles are reflected back to Earth, and the first signals to be returned may be well beyond the range of the ground wave. As a result there is an area between the maximum range of the ground wave and the area where the first sky-wave signals are heard where no signal may be audible. This area is known as the *skip zone* or the *dead zone* (**Fig 5.7**).

Critical frequency

The ionosphere is in a constant state of change. Accordingly it is very useful to be able to take measurements that give an indication of its current condition. One measurement that can be made relatively easily is known as the *critical frequency*. This is the frequency at which a signal that is directed vertically upwards just stops being reflected by a particular region in the ionosphere and passes on to the next region or into outer space. It is the highest frequency that can be reflected by a particular region.

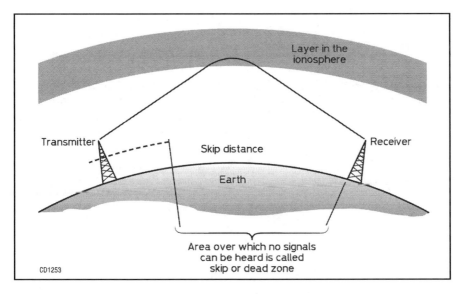

Fig 5.7: The skip or dead zone where no signal is audible.

The critical frequency is given the designation f_o. The subscript letter 'o' indicates that it applies to an *ordinary wave*. The ordinary wave is a wave that is reflected at the same height as it would be in the absence of the magnetic field. It is often termed the *O wave*. In contrast there is also an *extraordinary wave* that is affected by the magnetic field.

Each region has its own critical frequency, and this gives an indication of the state of the ionosphere. The critical frequency for the E layer is given the designation $f_o E$, while for the F2 layer it is designated $f_o F2$ etc. As might be expected, it varies from place to place and according to the time of day.

The critical frequency is measured by sending a radio pulse directly up into the ionosphere and monitoring the returned signal from a receiver co-located with the transmitter. The pulse is steadily moved up in frequency and readings taken over the relevant part of the spectrum. Initially a signal is returned and monitored. The time delay between the transmission of the pulse and its reception is used to determine the effective height (called the *virtual height*) of the region.

As the frequency is increased the signal is no longer reflected and passes through to the next region. Here it is initially reflected but as the frequency is again increased it eventually passes through. This process is repeated for all the regions and eventually the signal passes through the whole of the ionosphere and no reflection is received. The graphical data of the reflection height against frequency can be plotted to give what is termed an *ionogram* (see Chapter 8).

Maximum usable frequency

At any given time there is a maximum frequency that can be used to communicate between two locations by ionospheric propagation alone. Above this frequency signals pass through the ionosphere or may be reflected in

Region or layer	Distance (km)			
	1000	2000	3000	4000
Sporadic E	4.0	5.2	—	—
E	3.2	4.8	—	—
F1	2.0	3.2	3.9	—
F2 Winter	1.8	3.2	3.7	4.0
F2 Summer	1.5	2.4	3.0	3.3

Table 5.1. MUF factors for various distances assuming representative heights for the principal ionospheric regions.

a different way so that communication is not possible. This is known as the *maximum usable frequency* (MUF).

The fact that there is a maximum usable frequency most commonly results from the situation that as the transmission frequency is increased the signal penetrates further into the ionospheric layers until it passes straight through. When the point is reached where communications can just start to fail this is the maximum usable frequency. As a rule of thumb it is generally three (for the F region) to five (for the E region) times the critical frequency and it is true for low angles of incidence, although more exact methods are available for determining this figure.

It may be calculated from the relationship:

$$\text{MUF} = F/\sec\theta$$

In this relationship, θ is the angle the incident ray makes with a vertical line through the point of incidence. The factor $\sec\theta$ is called the *MUF factor* and it is a function of the path length if the height layer is known. By using typical figures for the heights of the different ionospheric regions, the factors shown in **Table 5.1** may be determined.

In some instances it may be necessary to restrict the MUF to a particular ionospheric mode. When this is necessary the values may be quoted together with an indication of the relevant mode, eg F2 MUF etc. In some instances reference may also be made to the ordinary and extraordinary waves. It is normally implied that figures are for the ordinary wave, but an X may be added, eg F2 MUF (X), for the extraordinary wave.

An *operational MUF* is also defined and may be seen in literature. This is the MUF that would permit acceptable operation of a radio service between given terminals under specific working conditions. In this definition the emphasis is on the operational acceptability of the circuit. It means that factors such as the antenna, power levels and such like are considered and gives an indication regarding the possibility of real communication at a given station.

Lowest usable frequency

Another parameter that is of great importance is known as the *lowest usable frequency* (LUF). If the frequency of a signal is reduced, then its strength at a receiving station will fall. This results from a variety of factors. One is that the D region attenuation increases, but in addition to this the signal will be reflected by lower regions in the ionosphere and this may result in further reflections and hops being required. Each reflection will introduce some loss. The overall effect is that there is a minimum frequency that will support communication between two stations.

The LUF is actually defined as the lowest frequency that would permit acceptable performance of a radio circuit by signal propagation via the ionosphere between given terminals at a given time and under specific working conditions. From the definition it can be seen that the LUF is dependent upon factors apart from the ionospheric propagation. Transmitter power, antenna gain and location, receiver characteristics and noise conditions all play their part. The type or mode of transmission is also important because wider bandwidths are required for transmissions such as SSB than for narrow-band modes like Morse or data communications. In view of the operational nature of the definition, it means that two stations located very close together, but having different equipment, may have very different figures for the LUF

It is possible to reduce the lowest usable frequency by changing factors such as the transmitter power or by employing a different mode of transmission that enables the receiver bandwidth to be narrowed. Antennas and the like may also be changed but this is unlikely to be feasible as a short-term measure. As a very rough guide, improving the circuit by about 10dB will reduce the LUF by about 2MHz.

A further point worth noting is that the LUF actually increases in periods of high solar activity. This is caused by the fact that the increased levels of solar radiation give rise to higher levels of ionisation in the D layer. This in turn increases the level of attenuation introduced by this layer. This means that at the peak of the sunspot cycle there is degradation in the performance of the lower-frequency bands for long-distance communications.

Optimum working frequency

It can be seen that over a very short period of time, the best frequency to use would be one close to the MUF. This offers the lowest levels of attenuation and usually the best overall performance. However, the changes in the ionospheric conditions over a period of time mean that it is unlikely to be reliable and a slightly lower frequency will be able to provide a more reliable service.

To account for this an *optimum working frequency* (OWF) is defined. The term *fréquence optimum de travail* (FOT) is also used and the abbreviation is possibly more commonly found than OWF. The OWF or FOT is the lower decile of daily values for the operational MUF at a given time over a given period, normally a month. In other words it is the frequency that is exceeded by the operational MUF for 90% of the time during the stated period. Here the emphasis of the definition is on the operational aspects of communication, rather than a broad figure indicating only the state of the ionosphere.

Path losses

There are many ways in which losses are introduced into signals that are propagated. The major one that has already been mentioned is the loss arising from the D region and in some instances from the lower regions of the E region.

Loss also arises from the fact that the signal spreads out as it travels, and the area covered by the wavefronts on the signal increase in area and accordingly the signal decreases in intensity.

Normally it might be expected that the distance travelled by the signal is that of the great circle distance between the transmitting and receiving stations. However, this is not exactly the case because the signal does not follow the curvature of the Earth but travels up to the ionosphere and then returns down again. As a result the distance that is travelled is larger than the great circle distance. Over paths where the angle of radiation is very low, the difference may be acceptably small but over other paths, where the angle of radiation from the antenna is much higher, there can be a significant difference. Accordingly higher levels of loss than expected might be experienced.

A further degree of loss is introduced by the fact that the polarisation of the signal can be changed by the ionosphere. Even though the signals that enter the ionosphere from terrestrial antennas are normally linearly polarised, the action of the ionosphere with the Earth's magnetic field results in the signal that emerges being elliptically polarised. Normally this loss is grouped together with a variety of other small losses. Its degree varies according to a number of factors, including the geomagnetic latitude, the season, time of day and the length of the signal path. Typically this loss may be around 9dB.

Fading

Fading and signal variations are major features associated with ionospheric propagation. The signal variations may be fairly shallow, with the signal changing in level between 10 and 20dB, or it may result in the signal completely disappearing. There are a number of reasons for this but they all result from the ever-changing state of the ionosphere.

One of the major causes is multi-path interference. Even with directive antennas the signal will illuminate a wide area of the ionosphere. As it is very irregular, the signal will reach the receiving station via a number of paths each with different path lengths and the overall received signal is the summation of them all. As the ionosphere changes, the signals will fall in and out of phase with one another, resulting in the strength varying by a considerable degree. See **Fig 5.8**. This may also be noticed on MF signals at night. Normally signals are audible via the ground wave during the day but at night the sky wave

Fig 5.8: A signal is received via several paths and, as changes occur in the ionosphere, signal lengths vary, causing signals to fall in and out of phase with one another. As a result the overall signal strength varies with time.

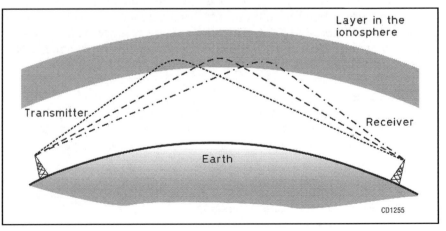

may also be audible. As the state of the ionosphere changes, so will the path length for the reflected signal, and accordingly the phase will vary. This will give rise to fading of the overall signal as the ground-wave and sky-wave signals interfere.

Irregularities in the ionosphere may also cause the path lengths of closely spaced frequencies to be different. For signals such as amplitude modulation (AM) and single sideband (SSB) this may result in a reduction in some frequencies in the audio range, while others are intensified. When this *selective fading* occurs serious distortion of an AM signal may occur if the carrier suffers the selective fading and a reduction in level. Since SSB signals do not depend on the transmission of a carrier, this mode is less affected by this form of fading. Synchronous detection of an AM signal also makes significant improvements in the signal quality under these conditions. The fact that there are appreciable changes in density of free electrons in the ionosphere gives rise to other forms of fading apart from path length changes. In one form of fading arising from this the ability of a region to reflect a signal at a given frequency may change. When operating near the MUF the signal may fade as the signal starts to pass through the region.

There may also be regions or clouds of high electron density in the D region. Accordingly, as the clouds move signals, especially those lower in frequency, will fade as the cloud passes through the signal path. Fading of this type normally takes place over a period of half an hour to an hour and may reduce the signal by a figure between 5 to 10dB.

A further type of fading occurs when the ionosphere causes changes in the polarisation of the signal. As it changes so will the strength of the signal picked up by the antenna depending on how closely its polarisation matches the antenna polarisation.

Multiple reflections

The maximum distance that can be achieved when using a reflection from the F2 region is around 4000km and for the other reflective regions in the ionosphere it is somewhat less. One reflection from the ionosphere does not explain how signals travel from the other side of the globe using ionospheric propagation. The reason is that signals undergo several reflections. After the signals return to Earth from the ionosphere they are reflected by the surface and returned back up to the ionosphere. Here they are reflected again by the ionosphere, being returned to the Earth a second time about twice the distance away from the transmitter that a single reflection would give. See **Fig 5.9**.

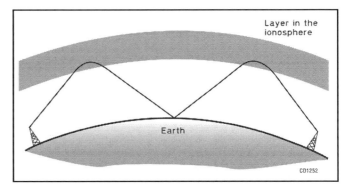

Fig 5.9: Several reflections and 'hops' can be used to enable greater distances to be achieved.

Unfortunately the signal undergoes additional attenuation, as might be expected. Each reflection by the Earth introduces some losses and therefore the signals are attenuated each time. The surface of the Earth at the point of reflection has a major effect on the level of these losses. Sea water is a very good reflector, as might be expected, but dry desert is very poor. This means that signals that are reflected in the Atlantic are likely to be stronger than those reflected by a desert region.

Apart from the reflection at the Earth's surface the signal suffers losses in the ionosphere as well. Every time the signal passes through the D region there is an additional amount of attenuation. This can be very important because the signal has to pass through the D layer twice each time it is reflected by one of the higher regions and, with more than one hop, the signal passes through the D region several times. As already mentioned, the attenuation reduces as frequency increases. Apart from the fact that high-frequency paths are more likely to use the F2 layer and have less reflections, the high-frequency path will also suffer less loss from the D layer. This will mean that a signal on 28MHz, for example, will be stronger than one on 14MHz, assuming that propagation can be supported at both frequencies.

It should also be remembered that the path length for a multiple-reflection signal will be greater than the great circle distance around the globe, especially if high angles of radiation are used. This in itself will add to the signal loss because the loss is proportional to the path length.

Chordal hop

At some times a tilt in the ionospheric regions, and in particular the F2 region, may occur. When this happens the signal may not be reflected back to Earth. Instead it is reflected so that it travels between the Earth and the ionosphere before meeting the ionosphere again where it can be reflected back to Earth (**Fig 5.10**). As this form of propagation does not involve a reflection from

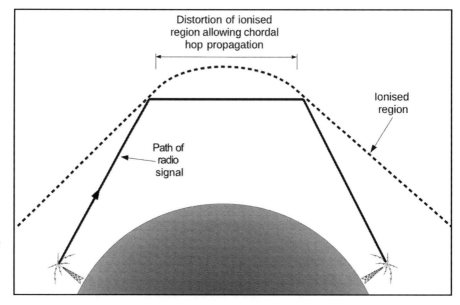

Fig 5.10: The north-south chordal signal path across the magnetic equator.

the surface of the Earth, the losses are much lower and accordingly signal strengths provided are higher. In some research it has been proposed that this form of propagation could account for round-the-world echoes.

The tilt or distortion in the ionosphere required to produce this form of propagation, known as *chordal hop*, occurs near sunrise and sunset and across the equator. The propagation using the equatorial anomaly generally occurs in a north-south (or south-north direction). The F2 region is higher across the equator and this means that either side of this it tilts, enabling the signals to be reflected above the Earth's surface.

Signal paths

There are a variety of mechanisms by which signals can propagate. With propagation over long distances the path may be a complicated summary of several hops utilising various regions. As the state of the ionosphere is not constant around the globe, reflections may use the F region in one area but the E region for signals on the same frequency in another. In some instances signals may even become trapped between the F and E regions where there is a valley in the level of ionisation, and interestingly MUFs for this mode of propagation are higher than they are for the equivalent path using a double hop.

A form of nomenclature has been devised to categorise the various paths that can be taken. Shown in **Fig 5.11**, it indicates the regions where the reflection takes place and a ground reflection is indicated by a hyphen between two letters. Thus F would indicate a single hop using the F region whereas E-F would indicate a reflection by the E region returning the signal to Earth where it is reflected back up to the F region before returning to Earth at the receiver.

Sporadic E

What is *sporadic E* (Es)? The best way to sum it up is to say that a quiet VHF or high HF band can suddenly come alive with strong signals from 1200km to 3000km away and then vanish just as quickly.

This transient nature of Es makes it a sought-after mode to boost the VHF locator square count in Europe, but multiple hop

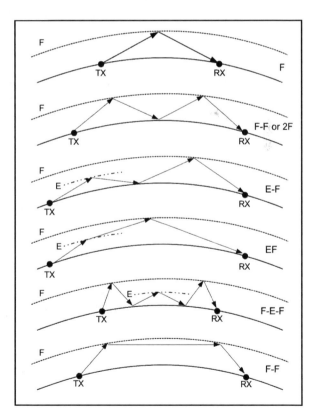

Fig 5.11: Some typical signal paths that may be taken along with the nomenclature used to describe them.

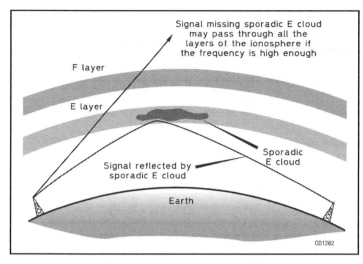

Signal missing sporadic E cloud may pass through all the layers of the ionosphere if the frequency is high enough

F layer

E layer

Sporadic E cloud

Signal reflected by sporadic E cloud

Earth

CD1262

Fig 5.12: The ionosphere and sporadic E.

Es paths can provide intercontinental DX to the States, for example, particularly on the 10m and 6m bands.

The basic principle is shown in **Fig 5.12**. There has been much learned about this mode during the last few years and, although there are still many uncertainties, ideas developed from continued research by radio amateurs (including QSO information submitted to *DX Clusters*) will allow the Es operator to gain new squares and miss fewer openings.

The essential finding is that the locations of many Es events at 90 – 120km are determined by the locations of certain weather events, or triggers, in the troposphere from the surface to 15km. This can help amateurs predict the better days to check for activity on bands from 10m through 6m, 4m and up to 2m on strong events, since there are plenty of sources of weather forecasts available to allow these 'triggers' to be found.

The most likely reason this link with weather appears to work is that turbulence created by weather events can produce ripples in the atmosphere (called *gravity waves*) that can propagate upwards to the E region, where they interact with the background winds there to produce something called *wind shear*.

This difference in wind speed and direction in the E region can focus ionisation, believed to be mostly from meteors, into dense enough patches to produce a sporadic E reflection point.

At one time many thought that thunderstorms were the cause of Es openings. But there are many examples of openings where there has been no thunderstorm activity whatsoever. Nevertheless, it remains as one of the possible factors in some Es openings.

Solar flares have also been implicated as providing the ionising radiation for some Es events. Indeed, there is compelling evidence that some smaller Es events outside of the main season have occurred just after a solar flare. But this hypothesis doesn't account for *all* sporadic E openings.

Essential facts

The main sporadic E season in the northern hemisphere is from May to August. There is a minor occurrence in mid-winter – December and January, so don't rule out those non-summer months entirely. But they are orders of mag-

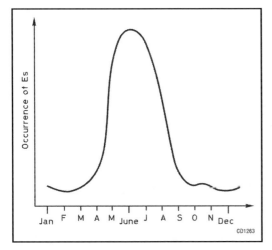

Fig 5.13: Occurrence of sporadic E in temperate regions of the northern hemisphere. NB: An equivalent curve can be noted for the southern hemisphere, but changed by six months.

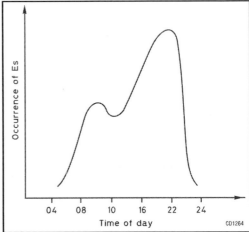

Fig 5.14: The likelihood of sporadic E openings occurring throughout the day in temperate regions.

nitude less reliable than the summer events, as can be seen in **Fig 5.13**. The daily pattern generally gives two peaks, one in late morning and a second, more noticeable, peak in late afternoon (**Fig 5.14**).

So if you hear on the *Cluster* that there has been an Es opening in the morning, definitely check again in the evening. The first obvious thing to do is check the beacon portion of the bands to see what paths might be opening. Various *Skimmer, WSPR* and *Reverse Beacon Networks* can all help paint a picture of what the ionosphere is doing.

As an Es event gets stronger, the higher frequency bands open up. The longest distance paths are usually on the highest band open, and indeed, those bands below it will experience progressively shorter skip distances as the event develops. So, if you hear really strong 'short skip' on 10m, then check 6m and upwards for possible Es.

The individual paths may be very fleeting, so there is no time for long overs, just a report and locator is usually safest. The event itself may span a few hours, but not necessarily to the same DX location. The Es clouds can vary greatly in size – they may only be a few metres across, whereas the large ones may be kilometres across.

Their shape also varies – some may be slightly circular in shape with approximately the same dimensions in both directions. Others may be relatively long and thin. While the shapes are not of great importance, they do help to explain why some stations may experience sporadic E propagation whereas others may not experience it or hear stations from totally different areas.

The small size of many Es clouds explains the 'spotlight' propagation effect that can occur. That is, it is quite possible for you to hear a distant station via Es, while a friend 10 miles away can hear nothing.

You can also get Es openings that extend right the way up to 144MHz (2m). These can be very short-lived, but you can usually rely on having at least one or two every summer. An important indicator that a VHF Es opening may soon occur is the presence of foreign broadcast radio stations on the FM Band II frequencies between 87.5 and 108.0 MHz. These stations, often from Spain or other parts of the Mediterranean, can be strong enough to override other more local stations in the UK at times.

The main weather triggers for Es appear to be jet streams in the troposphere, especially where they intersect with mountain ranges. Other weather elements can be guilty parties too, but jet streams are by far the main culprit.

The discussion forum on the RSGB website contains a daily map of jet stream locations produced by professional meteorologist Jim Bacon, G3YLA, plus Es discussion during the main Summer season. Go to **www.rsgb.org** then **main/forums/radio propagation questions/chart drawer**.

Not every jet stream produces Es, since a disturbed Earth's magnetic field can spoil the chances, as can the variations in the winds between the jet stream and E region, plus of course variations in the amount of meteor debris.

There are lots of uncertainties, but if you only do one thing, simply switch the rig on when you get home from work in the summer, before having your tea or cutting the lawn!

Spread F

Under some conditions the echoes which are received back from *ionosonde soundings* (see Chapter 8) of the ionosphere indicate that there are irregularities in the F layer. Instead of receiving a definite echo to give the effective height of the ionosphere at that frequency, a diffused or fuzzy echo is received (**Fig 5.15**). This phenomenon is known as *spread F* and is very common in some areas.

When spread F occurs the F layer does not consist of a layer with a uniformly varying level of ionisation as normally seen. Instead it appears as though turbulence has broken it up into various areas of differing levels of ionisation. These each reflect signals, giving a number of paths that the signal can take. Because the signal takes slightly different amounts of time to travel the different paths, when it arrives at the receiver it is a combination of a variety of components. This results in distortion and the flutter that is characteristic of signals that have travelled via a polar route. Signal levels are also lower because this method of reflection is not as efficient as normal F layer reflections.

Spread F occurs in two main areas. The first is around the equator

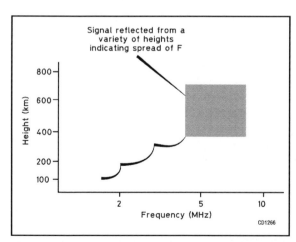

Signal reflected from a variety of heights indicating spread of F

Fig 5.15: Diagram of a typical ionogram indicating the presence of spread F.

between ±20° and invariably occurs at night. The second is at much higher latitudes above 40°, increasing with latitude to the extent that it is almost permanent in winter. This occurs mainly at night time but also sometimes in the day. There is little evidence of spread F occurring between latitudes of 20° and 40°. The regions affected by spread F may occur in patches (**Fig 5.16**), which may be as wide as several hundred kilometres. The patches drift horizontally at speeds of around 100m per second, always drifting eastwards in equatorial regions.

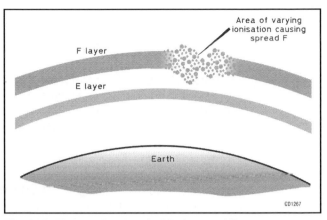

Fig 5.16: The mechanism behind spread F.

Interestingly the occurrence of spread F differs between the two regions. In equatorial regions spread F occurs on magnetically quiet days, and disappears with the occurrence of a magnetic storm. However, at higher latitudes it is linked with magnetic activity.

Grey-line propagation

At dawn and dusk signals are able to travel over much greater distances and with much lower losses than might normally be expected on some paths and frequencies. This occurs by what is termed *grey-line propagation* which occurs when signals travel along the grey or twilight zone between night and day. This area where night and day meet is also known as the *terminator*, and here signals on some frequencies are attenuated less than might normally be experienced – as a result signals can be received at surprisingly high levels over long distances.

The improved propagation conditions around the grey line occur primarily on the lower-frequency bands in the HF portion of the spectrum where the level of ionisation in the D layer is very

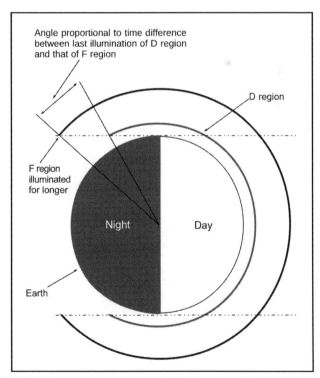

Fig 5.17: The F region remains illuminated for longer than the D region.

much reduced. This occurs while the level of ionisation of the F layer, which gives most of the long-distance signal propagation, is still high.

It happens for two reasons. The first is that the level of ionisation in the D region drops very quickly around dusk and after dark because the air density is high and recombination of the free electrons and positive ions occurs comparatively quickly. The second reason is that the F layer is much higher in altitude, and as the Sun sets it remains illuminated by the Sun's radiation for longer than the D region, which is lower down (**Fig 5.17**). Similarly in the morning when the Sun is rising, the F region receives radiation from the Sun before the D region and its ionisation level starts to rise before that of the D region. As the level of the D region ionisation is low, this means that the degree of attenuation to which the lower-frequency signals are subjected is very much less than in the day. This also occurs at a time when the F region ionisation is still very high and good reflections are still achievable. Accordingly this results in much lower overall path losses around the grey line than are normally seen.

When looking at the radio terminator region it should be remembered that there are a variety of variables that mean that it does not exactly follow the day / night terminator as seen on the Earth's surface. The ionised regions are well above the Earth's surface and are accordingly illuminated for longer, although against this the Sun is low in the sky and the level of ionisation is low. Furthermore there is a finite time required for the level of ionisation to rise and decay. As there are many variables associated with the radio signal propagation terminator, the ordinary terminator should only be taken as a rough guide for radio signal propagation conditions.

Frequencies that are affected by this form of propagation are generally limited to around 10MHz. This means that the bands primarily affected are the 80 (75), 40 and 30m bands. Frequencies higher in frequency are attenuated

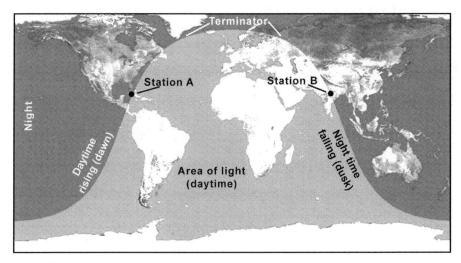

Fig 5.18: Grey-line type propagation conditions can be seen at higher frequencies as a propagation window opens between Station A and Station B.

to only a minor degree by the D region and therefore there is little or no enhancement.

It is, however, still possible for higher-frequency signals to be affected by a grey-line type enhancement. This occurs when a propagation path is opening in one area and closing in another, giving a short window during which it is open on a particular frequency or band of frequencies.

Looking at the MUFs over the course of the day can demonstrate the way in which this occurs. The level of ionisation in the F layer falls after dusk and rises at dawn. This results in the MUF falling after dark. Accordingly, stations experiencing dawn find the MUF rises and those experiencing dusk find that it falls. For frequencies that are above the night-time MUF, and for stations where one is experiencing dusk and the other dawn, there is only a limited time where the path will remain open. This results in a similar effect to that seen by the lower-frequency grey-line enhancement. See **Fig 5.18**.

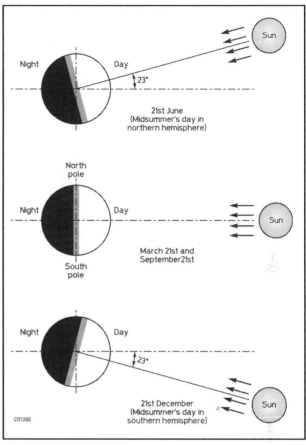

Fig 5.19: Grey-line paths change according to the time of year.

The path of the grey line changes during the course of the year (**Fig 5.19**). As the angle subtended by the Sun's rays changes with the seasons, so the line taken by the terminator changes. This results from the fact that during the winter months, the northern hemisphere of the Earth is tilted away from the Sun, and towards it during the summer months. The converse is obviously true for the southern hemisphere. In addition to this the width of the grey line also changes. It is much wider towards the poles because the line between dark and light is less well defined as a result of the fact that the Sun never rises high in the sky at the poles. It is also much narrower at the equator. This results in grey-line propagation being active for longer at the poles than at the equator.

Other dusk and dawn enhancements

A number of other enhancements have been noted at dusk and dawn, although they are less well documented and investigated. At times an enhancement of around 10dB has been noted at paths that cross the terminator line at 90°. Additionally a further useful effect is that just as the band is closing or opening, competition from those stations in the area for which the band is closed will be much less, and this can often be used to advantage.

John Devoldere's book *ON4UN's Low-Band DXing* confirms that paths perpendicular to the terminator may enjoy the greatest signal enhancement. That is, on the low bands, as sunset occurs at the receiving station, you may get enhancements at right angles to the terminator in the direction towards the dark side of the earth – not along the terminator.

Steve Nichols', G0KYA, own studies showed that twilight enhancements on 10m can occur when the signals cross the terminator at near right angles. On many occasions signals from Indian, Indonesian and other stations were heard in the UK on 10m just after their local sunset – these stations were not audible before. Brazilian station PT2GTI was also worked on 10m just after G0KYA's local sunrise, receiving a 59+ report using just 10 watts into an indoor dipole. He remained audible later that morning, but at reduced signal strengths, down 10 – 15db. The same type of enhancement was also seen with KP4NU in Puerto Rico.

So look for enhanced signals on 28MHz during local daytime in the UK from stations experiencing their local sunrise / sunset – from the west at their local sunset and from the east at their local sunrise.

There is an alternative way of looking at grey line conditions on 7MHz and 10MHz that is connected with the critical frequency (f_oF2). At frequencies above f_oF2 a radio wave travelling vertically upwards would pass through the F2 layer into outer space. Below f_oF2 it would be reflected back to earth. Now imagine a radio wave hitting the ionosphere at an angle of about 75 – 85° to the earth – a near vertical incidence wave (NVIS). This is looked at in more detail in the next section.

Below the critical frequency it would be returned. If it is some way above f_oF2 it will pass into space. But at some frequency close to f_oF2 it could be refracted through a large angle and end up travelling almost parallel to the earth, giving a very long first skip distance. This is the condition for the *Pedersen* or *critical ray*, discovered in 1927 and characterised as being high angle, long distance and close to, and probably above, the f_oF2 frequency. As there would be no intermediate ground hops the signal strength could be very high indeed.

It is likely that these conditions exist around local sunset / sunrise as the critical frequency changes and could account for long distance communications under grey line conditions on 7MHz and 10MHz.

Near vertical-incidence sky wave (NVIS)

NVIS is a very useful way in which sky-wave propagation can be used for short-haul communications. It is particularly suited to professional applications in geographical regions that are poorly served by land lines or line-of-sight repeaters, and it can provide a very useful and cost-effective alternative to satellite links. Even VHF regions in built-up or forested regions introduce very significant levels of loss, making line-of-sight VHF links virtually unworkable in many instances.

To use this form of propagation a near-vertical signal is launched towards the ionosphere at a frequency below the critical frequency. This signal is reflected by the ionosphere and returned to Earth over an area of many kilometres either side of the transmitter (**Fig 5.20**). In this way good local coverage can be obtained. This form of propagation is particularly useful in rough terrain because the coverage area is

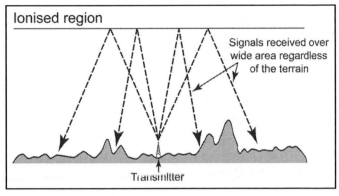

Fig 5.20: Near vertical incidence sky-wave propagation.

illuminated from above and undulations in the Earth's surface do not create shadow areas that cannot be reached. Typically radiation should be at angles greater than 75 or 80° to the horizontal so that good local coverage is achieved. Typically coverage areas may have a radius of between 35 and 350km. The frequency needs to be chosen carefully. Usually this is between about 2 and 10MHz, although during the periods of the sunspot minimum, maximum frequencies may be limited to below 7MHz. By using these frequencies, the losses from the D region can be overcome, and the higher layers of the ionosphere are still able to reflect the high-angle signals without them passing right through the ionosphere.

Chapter 6

Ionospheric disturbances, storms and auroras

The state of the Sun has a direct and very significant effect on the state of the ionosphere and ionospheric propagation. The solar disturbances can cause major disruption at some times, while at other times there may be enhancements, enabling communications either to be markedly improved or to be established via different forms of propagation.

The way in which the solar disturbances interact with the Earth's magnetosphere, and ultimately the ionosphere, is very complicated. Much of it is still not completely understood but research is ongoing and pushing the frontiers of our understanding so that a much better view of the mechanisms involved can be gained. Nevertheless, there is still a great amount that is well understood and this knowledge can be used to explain many of the phenomena that are observed.

Normal conditions

Before investigating the effects of solar disturbances on the ionosphere and radio propagation, it is worth summarising the way in which the Sun interacts with the Earth's magnetosphere and the ionosphere under quiet conditions.

Radiation from the Sun strikes the ionosphere to create the different ionised regions that refract / reflect radio signals. Also there is a continual stream of material flowing from the Sun in the form of the solar wind. This is normally deflected by the Earth's magnetic field so that the particles do not in general enter the atmosphere. However, when the Sun is disturbed the quiet conditions change, and radio propagation conditions can alter in a variety of ways and for a variety of reasons.

As solar disturbances have such a major impact on ionospheric propagation conditions they are reported in a variety of ways and by a number of different organisations.

In general there are three adverse effects on the ionosphere: geomagnetic storms, solar radiation storms, and radio blackouts, corresponding to the G, S, and R designations used in the WWV report at 18 minutes past each hour. They result from an increase in the level of radiation, very high-energy protons and, finally, an increase in the level of the solar wind, as shown in **Fig 6.1**.

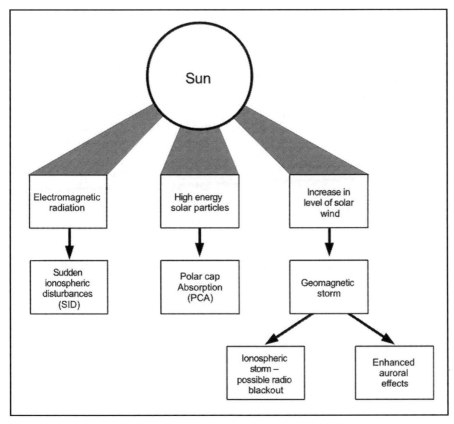

Fig 6.1: Summary of effects caused by solar disturbances.

Geomagnetic and ionospheric storms

Ionospheric storms can be very disruptive to ionospheric communications and can result in a complete blackout of ionospheric propagation. They occur when there is a geomagnetic storm, although not all such storms result in ionospheric storms.

All very large geomagnetic storms are now known to be caused by CMEs. Coronal holes can also also contribute large amounts of earth-directed plasma, especially during the declining phase of a solar cycle. These emit high-speed solar wind streams that can cause similar effects to a CME if the plasma has a south-facing Bz field that couples to the geomagnetic field.

During a CME vast streams of particles are emitted from the Sun, and if the stream is on a trajectory that intersects with the Earth it will have a significant impact. The stream takes between 20 and 40 hours to arrive and on Earth it is seen as a large increase in the speed and particle density of the solar wind, with the speed being the major factor in causing problems. When this increase arrives at the Earth a geomagnetic storm may occur when the level of magnetic activity changes and this can be seen by changes in the A and K indices (see Chapter 8) that can indicate the presence of a geomagnetic storm. These indices act as an indicator of the stability of the HF ionospheric propagation conditions.

The change in the magnetic activity is caused by particles entering the magnetosphere. As this happens they become trapped by the magnetic field and spiral around the lines of force between the northern and southern hemispheres, and they also drift around the Earth under the influence of the magnetic field. This motion is equivalent to a large electric current flowing around the Earth in the form of a ring. The current has an associated magnetic field that interacts with that of the Earth, giving rise to the changes known as a geomagnetic storm.

Usually the occurrence of a geomagnetic storm results in an ionospheric storm. When an ionospheric storm occurs, it changes the chemistry of the ionosphere in such a way that the levels of F region ionisation at high and middle latitudes are depressed by a significant degree. In turn this results in the maximum usable frequency reducing, often to half its value before the storm. The high-latitude E region is also affected in a similar way. There can also be an increased level of absorption in the D region levels, especially in the auroral zone.

Therefore the storm results in the maximum usable frequency falling as a result of the reduced levels of ionisation in the F region, and the lowest usable frequency rises as a result of the increased absorption. This means that the band of frequencies that can be used over a given path is greatly reduced. If the two frequencies (LUF and MUF) meet there is a complete radio blackout and no long-distance communications are possible over that path. During a severe storm it is possible that no stations from any direction may be heard over the whole of the HF spectrum via ionospheric propagation.

The onset of an ionospheric storm is relatively gradual. Previous warning may also have been given by the occurrence of other effects such as a *sudden ionospheric disturbance* (SID). However, the effects of the ionospheric storm are first noticed around the poles, after which they move outwards and may affect the whole of the globe, both sunlight and dark sides. Once under way the effects of the storm may be present for several days, with the effects of some severe storms being noticeable for periods of up to a week, although such long periods are relatively rare.

In view of the solar rotation period of 27 days this provides a natural reoccurrence period for these events. As a result of this, ionospheric storms often recur at this interval, but usually with a diminished intensity. Research has shown that the effects can persist for up to 10 solar rotations on rare occasions and this factor can be kept in mind when forecasting ionospheric propagation conditions.

Solar radiation storms

Solar disturbances may also eject vast quantities of high-energy protons. These typically take just over four hours to reach the Earth if they are on a trajectory that intersects it. As the stream of particles comes close to the Earth, the magnetic field prevents them from entering all around the atmosphere. Instead the particle stream is deflected towards the poles where they enter via the polar cap. Their entry results in a very large increase in the level of D region ionisation, and hence a much higher level of D region absorption, typically between 40 and 80dB on the lower frequencies.

This effect is known as *polar cap absorption* (PCA). The conditions appear quite suddenly and may last for up to three or four days. The PCA may totally black out radio communications across the polar cap on the lower frequencies. As it is fundamentally a D region attenuation effect, the level of attenuation falls with increasing frequency, although in view of the high levels of ionisation, the frequencies affected will be higher than those for normal D region ionisation. Users of the radio spectrum in other parts of the globe may not be aware of the blackout except that no signals are heard via polar paths across the polar cap.

Radio blackouts

Although CMEs are responsible for the longer-term disruptions to ionospheric propagation, solar flares can also cause disruption. One of the most commonly experienced effects of a big solar flare (M- or X-class) is a radio blackout or sudden ionospheric disturbance. It takes just over eight minutes for the radiation from the Sun to reach the Earth, at which point the effects start to be noticed. As light takes the same time to reach the Earth, there is no prior warning of an event happening.

The radiation caused by the flare comprises all forms of radiation, including a high level of X-rays which give rise to a high degree of ionisation in the D region, with the result that there is a very significant increase in the level of D region attenuation. Although the increase in the level of radiation is rapid, it takes time for the level of ionisation to rise. Consequently the lower frequencies are affected first and, as the degree of ionisation increases, so the higher frequencies are affected. During the day the D region normally affects frequencies up to 2 or 3MHz but the increase in radiation from a flare can cause much higher frequencies to be affected. In some cases it may result in a complete blackout on the HF bands, whereas at other times only the lower frequencies may be affected.

The D region is affected by the large increase in X-rays but other forms of radiation, including ultra-violet, also increase in intensity. This gives rise to an increase in the degree of ionisation in the higher regions of the ionosphere. This can result in an improvement in conditions on the higher-frequency bands, especially at the beginning of a radio blackout when the D region attenuation is not as high.

The radio blackout conditions may last up to a couple of hours, with the high-frequency bands recovering first as the D region ionisation falls and its attenuation decreases. Also, it is only the sunlit side of the Earth that is affected. Any areas that were in darkness when the flare occurred escape the effects. A further effect of a flare is that at the same time as the X-ray radiation reaches the Earth giving rise to a blackout, noise bursts from the increased levels of radio frequency radiation may be monitored at VHF.

These disturbances are called sudden ionospheric disturbances because they occur without any warning. They may also be called *short-wave fades*

(SWF) or the *Dellinger effect* after Dr Dellinger, who first noticed the effect and linked the degradation in propagation conditions to solar flares.

Auroras

One of the effects that can arise from a solar disturbance is an *aurora*. Also known as the *Northern* or *Southern Lights (Aurora Borealis* or *Aurora Australis)*, they are a magnificent sight in the skies (**Fig 6.2**). They appear as coloured glows, consisting of mainly white, green and red shades slowly changing with time. On some rare occasions a bluish glow may be seen. Sometimes the display can consist of coloured streamers that change their shape and colour over a period of a few minutes. Unfortunately these views are confined to areas around the poles, and can normally only be seen at latitudes greater than about 55°, although on some occasions when very large disturbances occur they have been seen much further away from the poles.

These displays are caused by free electrons from the increased solar wind entering the atmosphere around the magnetic poles. As the electrons descend they collide with other molecules in the upper atmosphere and release energy, some of which is light.

An aurora can occur after a CME. The arising increase in solar wind takes between 20 and 40 hours to arrive at the Earth and when it does the Earth's magnetic field diverts its particles from entering over the whole of the atmosphere. Instead they interact with the magnetosphere, causing electrons held there within the Van Allen belts to precipitate in the auroral zone areas around the poles.

The ionisation is caused in a number of ways. The free electrons that are precipitating from the magnetosphere have a very high energy and during their descent they collide with further neutrals to create further free electrons and positive ions. Typically one electron at 1keV will result in 300 free electron / positive ion pairs. In this way there are considerably more free electrons than those entering from the magnetosphere. As a result the levels of ionisation are extremely high.

In view of the very high electron densities in the polar regions it is possible for radio signals well into the VHF region to be reflected and for contacts to be made over considerable distances. The 50MHz and

Fig 6.2: The aurora borealis lights up the sky in Iceland. (Image: G0KYA.)

144MHz bands are the main ones where auroral contacts take place, although some contacts are possible on 432MHz. However, the path is not nearly as good on 432MHz where signals are around 30 or 40dB weaker than on 144MHz. Although the path deteriorates rapidly with frequency, professional studies using ionospheric radar soundings have detected reflections, even though very weak, at frequencies in the region of 3GHz.

Auroral propagation can only take place relatively close to the poles. Generally stations must be located at latitudes greater than 55°, although during large auroras stations well outside these bounds may be able to hear the effects.

To utilise auroral propagation signals should be directed towards

Fig 6.3: Typical beam headings required to use auroral propagation.

the auroral region and not towards the station with whom a contact is to be made. This is because signals are heard by *backscatter*, where the signal is reflected back in a similar overall direction to that from which it arrived. In general antennas should be pointed northwards for the northern hemisphere and southwards in the southern hemisphere so that the signal is reflected from the auroral zone or front. The optimal beam headings may vary considerably depending upon the location of the auroral front, the station being contacted and the prevailing conditions. See **Fig 6.3**. Signals that are reflected using auroral propagation are badly distorted and as a result Morse is normally the preferred mode. The distortion results from the fact that the state of the ionosphere changes very rapidly as the electrons precipitate from the magnetosphere. This causes very rapid fading to occur that manifests itself as a rough low-frequency buzz of around 50 to 60Hz. This buzz changes very much in nature from one aurora to the next, and even during the course of an auroral event.

In addition to the buzz, the signals are Doppler shifted because the electrons form a moving reflector as they stream down to Earth. This can give a frequency shift of up to 1kHz or so at 144MHz. Shifts on other frequencies are proportional to the frequency in use and are less on 50MHz and greater on the higher frequencies. Due to the fact that the electrons do not all move at exactly the same rate, there is a spread in the degree of frequency shift and this adds a form of 'hiss' to the signal.

The combined result of the buzz and hiss means that Morse signals have a very distinctive note. It also makes single sideband (SSB) signals difficult to copy. The degree of buzz and hiss is more pronounced, the higher the frequency in use, and this means that it is easier to copy SSB signals at 50MHz than 144MHz.

It can be very useful to be able to predict the onset of an auroral event. One useful guide is known as a *pre-auroral enhancement* and occurs on the HF bands. This arises because just before an auroral event the level of ionisation in the ionosphere can rise, although this generally happens in the middle to low latitudes. It first affects the F region and this leads to an enhancement in the HF propagation conditions. After this has occurred the ionospheric storm appears. At this point the HF conditions may fail, and this is the time to look for auroral propagation in the VHF portion of the spectrum.

Further indications about the onset of auroras can be gained from the A and K indices to be described in Chapter 8. When these figures rise to the storm levels it is a good indication that a storm is likely or actually under way. These figures can be obtained from a variety of propagation-related sites on the Internet.

A further point to note is that ionospheric storms tend to re-occur at 27-day intervals, corresponding to the rotational period of the Sun. Although changes in the HF conditions have been noted up to 10 rotations of the Sun, the maximum for auroral events is normally three or four times.

During an auroral event it can be seen that there are daily fluctuations that occur as a result of the normal daily changes in the ionosphere and the increase of the solar wind. Although it is not possible to set down exact rules as there are so many fluctuations there are some rough guidelines that can be mapped out. Normally events do not commence until around 1300 local time at the earliest. It is actually more usual for them to commence in the mid-afternoon, and continue until about 1900. After this, activity subsides and it is not normally possible to make any contacts around 2000. Later a second phase may occur between about 2100 and 2300. A third phase may then occur between about midnight and 0600 with no possibility of contacts between 2300 and 2400.

It is also found that some auroral events have no afternoon or late-evening phase, only having an after-midnight phase. When this occurs, it may herald a much larger event the following day. The times here refer to winter times, and adjustment should be made for the conversion to summer daylight saving time at the relevant times of year.

Chapter 7

Propagation on the LF and MF bands

While we have looked at solar flares and geomagnetic storms, their effects on the LF and MF bands can be very different from those on HF. After introducing the mechanisms behind geomagnetic disturbances in the last chapter, it is worth looking at them in more detail, and also introduce the concept of the *Disturbance storm time index* (Dst). This will help us understand LF and MF propagation better. Much of the information in this chapter comes courtesy of Alan Melia, G3NYK, a keen LF enthusiast.

The first thing to say about propagation on the LF and MF bands is that it is very different from that experienced on HF. The major difference is that where HF signals are refracted back towards the Earth's surface by the F-region of the ionosphere, LF, VLF, and low MF signals cannot pass through the lower D and E regions. Long distance propagation is therefore dependent on these regions. That is, MF and LF signals can be 'bounced' off the D and E regions, when HF signals may either be attenuated by them or simply pass through to the higher F region(s).

As you read earlier, whereas the F region exists at around 250 to 600km, the D-region is at 50 to 90km with the E-region above it.

The variations in propagation conditions that we see are due to variations in the charge density caused by variation in the radiation from the Sun.

These LF signals can still propagate via the ground wave, but sky wave LF signals have different characteristics to HF ones.

Fading

At some distance around 400 to 700km, depending on the power of the transmitter and noise levels at the receiver, the ground wave and ionospheric wave may arrive at the receiver at roughly the same strength.

This leads to problems at short ranges on 475kHz because the path distances of the two components of the received signal are different, and the ionospheric (often called sky wave) path length varies as the ionisation level changes. This leads to severe fading. When the sky wave and ground wave arrive in phase the signals add but when they are 180° out of phase they cancel, and the resulting signal is equal to the difference in amplitudes over the two paths.

Thus if the two paths produce signals at the same amplitude, the received signal will disappear completely as the phase difference passes though 180°.

Day-time range

The maximum daytime range on 475kHz for one traverse of the ionosphere can be estimated. If we assume an 'apparent reflection height' of 50km then the range works out at about 1000km. At this range the sky wave is stronger than the ground wave so that fading is reduced from that seen at short ranges. However, because amateur power are limited and signals are often close to local noise levels, fading can make reception difficult.

Night-time range

The daytime ionisation that produces the D-layer is due to to hard solar ultra-violet radiation and soft X-rays. These are shadowed at sunset and the D-layer ionisation recombines rapidly. This results in the apparent reflection height increasing to the upper D-region or even the lower E-layer. The E-region starts at about 100km where the remaining atmosphere is extremely thin.

The ionisation is due to cosmic rays and some charge from the solar wind, but because the density is low the recombination time is much longer and the E-layer persists for the whole of the darkness period.

If we perform a geometric calculation for a 100km reflection we see a maximum one-hop range of just over 2000km. Thus the best long distance contacts are made when both the transmitting and receiving stations are in darkness.

When talking about darkness it is of course the state of the ionosphere we must consider. So it is possible to make a good contact towards the west up to an hour after ground sunrise, And signals may be received from the east about a hour before sunset.

Multi-hop propagation

After one hop the signal at maximum range approaches the ground at a grazing incidence. At this point the wave may skip across the contact point and start rising towards the ionosphere again as the ground falls away again.

If we consider the path from western Europe to to the east coast of the USA the path is around 6000 to 7000km making this a three-hop path at night on the basis of our simple geometric model.

A careful observation by Alan Melia, G3NYK, of the path from the UK to VO1NA in Newfoundland on 136kHz (a 4500km path from the UK) showed that on some nights the path opened when the sunset shadow reached mid-Atlantic at 100km altitude, which suggests that there was a weak single-hop signal.

The three-hop path to the east coast of the USA sometimes shows a similar effect, with an opening starting when the shadow reached two-thirds of the way across the Atlantic.

These observations suggest that there can be a number of multi-hop paths viable at the same time.

The phase differences due to the different distances travelled by the different modes lead again to fading effects, but there is generally no ground wave signal of any significant strength reaching the receiver.

Solar flares

Earlier we looked at solar flares – vast eruptions of electromagnetic energy on the Sun's surface, in a wide spectrum from radio waves to X-rays that can be detected optically.

To recap, the ultra-violet portion of this flare affects the ionosphere on the daylight side of the Earth only. Its effect is to greatly increase the level of ionisation in the lowest D-region. This produces a strongly absorbing D-layer at HF and what is referred to as a Dillinger fade-out on the HF bands.

But the effect on LF and MF is totally different. This burst of high-intensity radiation ionises the D-region so intensely that it will return an LF / MF signal from its lowest extent.

Most flares are relatively short events lasting a few minutes at most, though there are occasional long-tail flares that can persist for around an hour.

Geomagnetic storms

Geomagnetic storms were observed to cause a decease in LF signal strength on long paths when these bands were used for world-wide communications in the 1920s.

It was also noticed that the signals did not recover immediately after the storm had passed and the K index returned to low values. It was discovered that the stronger the storm the longer the poor conditions would last.

The Equatorial Ring Current

The cause of the long-delayed recovery of LF / MF propagation after a geomagnetic storm was not recognised until after the discovery and exploration of the Van Allen belts.

Whilst the ions rotate over the equator the lighter electrons circle the north-south lines of magnetic force being reflected onto a reverse path as the lines bunch together near to the poles. This trapped charge is supplied by the solar wind, and the state of the rings can be detected by the changes they induce on the normal geomagnetic field.

When a CME or coronal hole plasma cloud approaches the Earth and collides with the Earth's magnetosphere (the sheath of force lines generated by currents in the Earth's molten iron core) there are two possible outcomes. These depend upon the direction of the magnetic field carried by the CME. If the field is opposing the Earth's field (north pole to north pole) the plasma cloud 'bounces off' the magnetosphere. There may be small disturbances seen on magnetometers, but there is generally no effect on LF / MF propagation.

If, however, the fields 'connect' (north pole to south pole), there are weak points in the magnetosphere at the poles where charged particles may enter the magnetosphere and even the atmosphere. In this latter case they produce strong auroral effects often far south of normal aurora sightings. Some charge also enters the *ring current*. The residue is guided round the magneto-sphere and becomes trapped in the magneto-tail on the side of Earth remote from the Sun.

As the charge in the tail builds up, the magnetic field there becomes very distorted, like a wound-up elastic band. Eventually the energy in the tail is released as the magnetic field snaps back to a lower energy state and like its start at the solar surface this propels two masses of the trapped plasma in opposite directions. One is towards Earth where, because it is now inside the magnetosphere, it enters the ring current, and onwards towards the outer solar system.

The Dst Index

The state of the ring current is measured by the *Disturbance storm-time* (Dst) index, which measures the magnetic field due to the circulating charge in the ring current.

Field measurements are taken by a number of observatories and corrected to represent the equivalent field at the Earth's equator. The field due to the ring current varies between 20nT in quiet conditions and 500nT in a severe storm. This value has to be measured as a deviation against the geomagnetic field, which has a value of 50,000nT (50µT). Dst values are only quoted after significant averaging and processing to remove rogue values.

Kyoto university produces an hourly real-time chart of their estimate of the Dst index, which is continually 'massaged' to remove rogue readings. (To find it you can Google 'Kyoto Dst Index'). Colorado University also publishes plots of their estimate on a real-time basis, but their estimate is based on measurements derived from the ACE satellite, and it plots this together with the Kyoto values.

At this stage one might wonder where all this is leading, but a quick look at one of the Dst plots (**Fig 7.1**) shows that they do in fact mirror the propagation on the LF / MF bands. There is a deep dip in the Dst after a CME impact: the Dst drops from −20 nT to a value greater than −100nT, but then returns slowly following a logarithmic curve over the following days. This can be explained by considering the ring current as a reservoir of energetic (hot) electrons that

Fig 7.1: The Kyoto Dst index showing a massive dip around midnight on 21 December 2015. The Kp index hit five around this time due to incoming solar plasma.

enter the ionosphere at sunset and sunrise when the magnetosphere is distorted by the solar wind pressure as parts of the Earth move to face the Sun.

This distortion allows the electrons to 'leak out' of their magnetic bottle and enter the ionosphere, diffusing away from the polar regions.

These hot electrons have the same effect on radio propagation as the photo-dissociated electrons produced by electro-magnetic radiation from the Sun in daytime. The difference is that they are 'hot', or moving very fast. This means that if they encounter an ion or atom in the atmosphere they will tend to bounce off, losing little energy in the process. This means that the so-called 'precipitated electrons' (those from the ring current) take much longer to decay, or be captured. Some plots of station strength after a CME impact show the signal recovering at the rate of about 5dB per hour, whereas the photo-dissociated electron in the D-layer decay almost immediately the radiation is removed.

This does not explain why, after severe storms, the propagation may be depressed for up to 30 days, except you may remember that injection occurs at the sunrise and sunset edges.

The Dst can be considered as a measure of the quantity of charge in the ring current, and the logarithmic recovery suggests a concentration-driven diffusion process.

Thus the recovery of the propagation conditions seems to follow closely the Dst, which can be used to estimate the length of a period poor conditions. It also shows how the period is extended when the ring current charge is 'topped up' by further CMEs.

LF / MF propagation usually starts to display 'good' conditions when the Colorado University Dst estimate has a numerical value greater than about −20nT. However, this is not the only effect causing changes in propagation, and just because the Dst is −20nT it does not guarantee that there will be good propagation.

This is demonstrated by a plot of the signal strength from an LF military station, the Canadian Naval station, callsign CFH, located at Newport Corner just outside Halifax in Nova Scotia and transmitting on 137kHz (**Fig 7.2**). During 2003 it was transmitting continuously with a steady radiated power of 20kW. The signal as received on the east coast of the UK was recorded with samples every minute. This

Fig 7.2: *From this graph you can see that better long-distance LF propagation generally occurs when the Dst index recovers and is better than −60nT.*

data was re-analysed recently to plot the propagation against the Dst in the preceding 12 hours.

The propagation was defined as the percentage of the time the signal exceeded a given strength, as a proportion of the darkness hours for the path. The plot shows that there is a sharp cut off around −60nT as the Dst index is depressed.

It should be noted that this path is around 4000km so is a two-hop path. Two passages through the ionosphere mean two doses of attenuation. The longer multi-hop paths are more sensitive to this attenuation than 1000km paths around Europe, though these will show poor results for signals close to the signal-to-noise threshold.

The region of precipitation is around the magnetic poles and the hot electrons diffuse away from that point. Thus the effect of the attenuation is reduced for paths at lower latitudes. This was demonstrated by observations of apparently good propagation from southern Europe to the French island of Reunion in the Indian Ocean at the same times as North Atlantic paths from Newfoundland to Europe were being heavily attenuated.

Conversely high-latitude paths such as Europe to Alaska suffer immediate high attenuation plus effects due to the aurora curtain and *polar cap absorption* (PCA), which is caused by proton storms.

This gives a broad idea of the propagation features of the LF bands. A basic understanding will hopefully assist in trying to select the right transmission modes for a particular path.

In particular the fading period due to multipath effects varies with the band used and as the frequencies move higher so the fading gets to be more rapid.

It is essential to select a transmission mode that is not made incomprehensible by long deep fades. Propagation varies over the year and in winter it is often possible to hear Newfoundland stations well into daytime, and for a European station to be heard well before sunset in North America.

Very long paths such as Europe to Australia have been claimed and often the times indicate that darkness did not exist over the complete signal path.

Very occasional contacts have caught the lift of an unpredictable solar flare for improved daylight range.

Some of the early transatlantic crossings on 136kHz were made due to them coinciding with favourable fading for long enough to complete the contact.

Chapter 8

Predicting, assessing and using ionospheric propagation

I t is very important for many users of the HF portion of the radio spectrum to be able to assess and predict propagation conditions. For example, international short-wave broadcasters need to know which frequencies will enable them to reach their target areas best, and this has to be planned months in advance so that frequencies can be arranged and new service schedules can be determined. For radio amateurs and short-wave listeners the conditions are of particular importance because they enable estimates of when to listen for stations from particular areas. If a beam is used, it enables the beam to be directed to areas where propagation conditions may be best supported. These and many other reasons make estimates of propagation of great interest.

To cater for all these needs various techniques are used, and a science akin to weather forecasting has been built up. Using a variety of measurements it is possible to detect the state of the ionosphere at a particular time, and using other methods it is possible to predict the propagation conditions in the future. However, like weather forecasting there are many factors that influence the state of the ionosphere and other regions that govern the way the radio signals propagate. As a result these predictions can never be totally accurate. This means that experience and the 'know-how' of the radio operator can enable the best to be made of the actual prevailing conditions. The different portions of the radio spectrum use different mechanisms to enable signals to be propagated. Below frequencies around 30MHz the ionosphere plays a major role in the way signals propagate, but above this the troposphere and line-of-sight communications are more important.

A broad summary of the propagation modes used is given in **Table 8.1** on the next page.

Amateur band summaries

There are many amateur bands located throughout the radio spectrum and several of these use ionospheric propagation. From LF through to the top of the HF portion of the spectrum there is a total of 12 bands. Even though many of them are relatively close to one another, the nature of each one is different and has its own distinct 'character'. As such it is possible to utilise each

Band	Frequencies	Principal propagation modes
VLF	3–30kHz	Ground wave, waveguide formed with ionosphere
LF	30–300kHz	Ground wave, waveguide formed with ionosphere
MF	300–3000kHz	Ground wave, sky wave and ionosphere (particularly E region)
HF	3–30MHz	Sky wave and ionosphere (E, F1, F2 regions), also sporadic E
VHF	30–300MHz	Line of sight, sometimes with tropospheric enhancement, sporadic E, meteor scatter at low end of spectrum, auroral reflections towards higher latitudes
UHF	300–3000MHz	Line of sight, sometimes with tropospheric enhancement
SHF	3–30GHz	Line of sight, troposcatter, rainscatter

Table 8.1: A broad summary of the propagation modes applicable to different portions of the radio spectrum.

one in a slightly different way, enabling the best to be made of the prevailing propagation conditions.

136kHz (135.7 – 137.8kHz)

This is the lowest frequency band currently available to UK amateurs and was allocated to the Amateur Service at WRC-07 in 2007. Although the maximum power is restricted to 1 watt ERP, in practice this is quite difficult to achieve given the problems of building an antenna large enough to be very efficient.

Large antennas with good earth systems are required to ensure that the antenna efficiency is raised to sufficiently high levels, as the size of antennas that can normally be erected compared to their wavelength means that efficiency levels are normally low.

Because of the small size of the band, IARU Region 1 agreed to restrict modes having a bandwidth of 200Hz or less. Operation is usually CW or QRSS CW (very low speed CW), and narrow band digital modes.

Using these techniques it is possible for stations to be heard commonly over distances of 100 miles or more. Beyond this, signals may be heard over distances of several hundred miles. However, occasional transatlantic contacts have been made.

472kHz (472 – 479kHz)

This band was allocated to the Amateur Service at WRC-12. Although not yet released to the Amateur Service in all countries, UK amateurs holding a Full Licence may use the band subject to specific conditions in the licence frequency schedule.

The IARU has not agreed a band plan as yet, but it is expected that as more countries gain access to the band, it will be discussed and implemented in the near future. In general, CW is in the lower part of the band, up to about 475kHz, and data modes above.

Propagation is similar to that found in the 136kHz band, with similar issues surrounding the size of the antennas required.

160m (Top Band) (UK allocation 1.81 – 2.0MHz, US allocation 1.80 – 2.00MHz)

This is the lowest frequency band in what is thought of as the short-wave part of the radio spectrum, although it is actually in the MF portion of the spectrum rather than the HF section. In view of its status with the longest wavelength (disregarding 136kHz that was not allocated when its name was first used), it is often referred to as *Top Band*. The actual allocations between different countries vary slightly as demonstrated by the difference between the UK and US allocations. However, many other countries have smaller allocations.

As the band is in the MF portion of the spectrum, signals are heard via ground wave during the day as sky-wave signals are completely absorbed by the D region. The distances that may be achieved are dependent upon a variety of factors including the transmitter powers, antennas (vertical polarisation is best for ground wave) and the nature of the terrain between the transmitter and receiver. Sandy areas are not good for propagation, whereas moist areas provide much better propagation. Signals travel best over the sea as it provides a good medium over which ground-wave signals may propagate and the signals do not need to diffract around hills (unless there are islands with hills in the signal path). In general it should be possible for signals to be heard via the ground wave over most types of terrain for distances of around 75km.

At night the D region ionisation disappears and the distances that can be achieved greatly increase. Often propagation uses the lower parts of the E region and some attenuation is introduced during each reflection. Nevertheless many signals are audible over distances of 1000km and more and often communications are possible across the Atlantic. On some occasions it is possible to establish communications with stations on the other side of the globe, although for long-distance contacts it is essential that very effective antennas are used by both stations.

Timing is very critical for long-distance contacts because the propagation paths may only be available for a short time. In some instances the openings may only last a few minutes. It is essential that the path remains in darkness to ensure that D region attenuation is not present, although there are short dawn and dusk improvements, especially for contacts with stations at the other side of the globe, which may only last for a few minutes. For transatlantic communications, the paths may be open for several hours but they generally peak when it is sunrise or sunset at the relevant end of the path. It is also found that north-south paths generally peak around midnight.

As a general rule long-distance work improves in winter because of the longer hours of darkness and lower levels of static. Additionally the fact that radiation of the ionosphere is absent for longer means that the residual D region ionisation is lower and levels of attenuation from this and also the lower reaches of the E region are minimised.

Unfortunately winter in the northern hemisphere corresponds to summer in the southern hemisphere and this means that there is no optimum time of year for cross-hemisphere contacts and these may be undertaken during any season.

80m (UK allocation 3.5 – 3.8MHz, US allocation 3.5 – 4.0MHz)

As this band is higher in frequency than 160m, there is a greater possibility of long-distance contacts. During the day stations that are a few hundred kilometres distant may be heard as high-angle signals are able to penetrate the D region. Then at night as the D region ionisation falls, so the distances over which stations can be heard increase. To achieve good results, efficient antennas are required. Although it is possible to establish some long-distance communications, the high levels of static and other noise mean that good signals must be transmitted if they are to exceed the level of noise at the receiving station.

Again the long-distance paths must remain in darkness for communications to be possible, although grey-line propagation can produce some spectacular results. Here it is often possible to hear stations from the other side of the globe peaking with signal strengths that may appear to be the same as local stations. The optimum time for these contacts is during the spring and autumn. Skip can be very selective as signals may at first be completely inaudible but with stations in slightly different areas hearing the long-distance signals at good strength. Then as the skip varies signals may increase, while they fade out with the first stations to hear the long-distance signals.

In general the performance of 80m for long-distance communications improves toward the low end of the sunspot cycle. This arises from the fact that ionisation levels are lower, and in particular the ionisation of the D region is lower. This brings lower levels of attenuation for this band.

60m (5MHz)

The UK's allocation at 60m is not a band as such, but a collection of small frequency segments that lie between 5258.5 and 5406.5kHz. At WRC-15 in November 2015, the amateur service also achieved a new 15kHz secondary allocation between 5351.5 – 5366.5kHz. This was not yet in effect at the time of writing.

The 5MHz allocation lends itself to inter-G contacts using NVIS propagation. This can be useful at times when the critical frequency (f_oF2) is below 7MHz, but daytime D layer absorption on 80m (3.5MHz) precludes contacts around the UK on that band.

Activity from stations outside the UK can also be found on 5MHz, with many different allocations including countries that are limited to a few spot frequencies.

40m (UK allocation 7.0 – 7.2MHz, US allocation 7.0 – 7.3MHz)

This is often considered to be one of the low-frequency bands in the HF spectrum and as a result it often does not receive the attention that it deserves. In fact it can produce some surprisingly good results. During the day stations may be heard up to distances of several hundred kilometres. Distances much beyond this are not common during the day because only signals with a high angle of incidence are heard. Low-angle signals have further to travel through the D layer and they suffer greater levels of attenuation. This means that the skip zone is either very small or non-existent.

At night the D region ionisation level falls and the distances over which signals can be heard greatly increases. The strength of local stations falls as the skip distance increases and this considerably reduces the level of interference, making long-distance communications far easier. There are also considerable dawn and dusk enhancements that can be used to great advantage, and these typically last for longer than on 3.5MHz as the degree of attenuation introduced by the D region is less.

30m (UK and US allocations 10.100 – 10.150MHz)

This band was released after the World Administrative Conference (WARC) held in 1979. As it is only 50kHz wide, the IARU recommends that only narrow-band modes, such as Morse and some data modes, be used on 30m.

The propagation is very similar to that experienced on 40m except that the level of D region attenuation is less during the day. This means that daytime propagation using lower angles of incidence can be supported and the distances that can be achieved are slightly greater. It is also found that a skip or dead zone is present, except during periods around the sunspot peak when D region ionisation levels will be greater.

In general, the level of absorption is less than on 40m, and during the night distances increase, providing world-wide communications. Propagation is best when the path lies in darkness but again conditions are enhanced at dawn and dusk, although this is less much less marked than on the lower-frequency bands.

20m (UK and US allocations 14.00 – 14.35MHz)

This is the mainstay, long-haul band providing the possibility of contacts over 1500km at most times, and possibility of communications over much greater distances at some time virtually every day. Here the level of D region attenuation has generally fallen to the degree that it is not a major factor and the band offers the possibility of good long-distance contacts during the day via the F2 region.

At night, during the sunspot minimum and in the winter the band normally closes and no signals are heard because the ionisation level of the F region falls to such a degree that the MUF is below 14MHz. However, during the summer the band generally remains open for much or all of the night, especially during periods of the sunspot maximum. It is generally found that spring and autumn bring the best conditions, particularly for contacts between the northern and southern hemispheres when stations from the opposite hemisphere may be heard at various times of the day.

17m (UK and US allocations 18.068 – 18.168MHz)

This band, which was released by WARC 1979 for amateur use, is another useful long-haul band. It possesses many of the characteristics of the 20m band, being mainly a daytime band with the possibility of operation at night during the summer and the periods of the solar maxima. However, being slightly higher in frequency it requires that the MUFs are higher and therefore it will not always remain open as long as the 20m band.

15m (UK and US allocations 21.00 – 21.45MHz)

This is one of the long-haul bands that has been available for very many years. As it is higher in frequency than the 20m band it may not remain open as long, but again its higher frequency means that long-haul stations can be heard at good strength. However, it is more variable and is affected by the prevailing conditions more. Near the peak of the solar cycle the band is open during the day and well into the night when stations can be heard over many thousands of kilometres. When the band is open like this, signal strengths are usually better on this band than 20m because it is higher in frequency and D region attenuation is less. However, conditions are usually not quite as good in the early morning because it takes some time for the ionisation levels to rise sufficiently to support communications. During the sunspot minimum few stations may be heard during the day and none at night because MUFs may not rise sufficiently high to support communications on these frequencies.

A good indication of the state of the band may be gained by listening to stations in the broadcast band above 21.45MHz. If no stations are audible it is likely that no amateur signals will be heard.

12m (UK and US allocations 24.89 – 24.99MHz)

Another of the WARC 1979 bands, this is higher in frequency than 15m and as such provides a good opportunity for daytime long-haul contacts. It is less likely to be open into the evening than 15m as it is higher in frequency and MUFs tend to fall after dusk. As a daytime band it offers the possibility of a good number of long-haul contacts, although it is greatly affected by the solar cycle and there will be long periods during the solar cycle minimum where the band is not open except by sporadic E.

10m (UK and US allocations 28.00 – 29.70MHz)

This band is right at the top of the HF portion of the radio spectrum. As such it is the most variable of the short-wave bands, but when it is open it offers excellent possibilities, especially for stations using low power levels or for those with poor antennas. The reason for its performance is that D region attenuation is exceedingly low and even low-angle signals are hardly attenuated.

Against this the band suffers from long periods during the solar or sunspot minima when it is completely closed to F region propagation. The only mode of propagation by which signals may be heard over any distance during these periods is by sporadic E, which occurs relatively frequently in summer months in temperate zones. In equatorial zones sporadic E is more common and appears all the year round. However, distances that may be covered by sporadic E are less than by reflection by the F region, although some double-hop propagation can occur on occasions.

Monitoring conditions

There are several methods that can be used to monitor the actual conditions and state of the bands. Sounders may be used to test the state of the ionosphere but one of the most reliable methods is to monitor stations from around the world to find out to which areas the propagation paths are actually open. This can be time consuming and unreliable if undertaken in a random fashion, but a variety of beacon stations have been set up to enable propagation conditions to be monitored either on a casual or an ongoing basis.

Beacons

There is a series of frequencies and sub-bands within the amateur bands that are set aside for the operation of beacons. These transmit throughout the day on specific frequencies, and by monitoring the transmissions along with knowledge of their locations it is possible to gain an accurate view of the prevailing propagation conditions. This can be useful for determining which bands provide the best opportunities for communications with specific areas as well as for long-term studies of propagation.

The first beacons to be set up were allocated individual frequencies, and there is a sub-band in the 10m band that is reserved for this purpose. While the beacons are very useful, if they are on a variety of frequencies it is not always easy to gain a quick idea of propagation conditions.

To provide a more effective service and to utilise less bandwidth an internationally co-ordinated network of beacons has been organised for use on the HF bands. The International Beacon Project has up to 18 stations around the world transmitting on frequencies of 14.100, 18.110, 21.150, 24.930 and 28.200MHz. The beacons share the same frequencies but are time multiplexed, ie they transmit at different times. In this way a receiver needs only to be tuned to a single frequency to discover which paths are open. Each beacon transmits in turn, with transmissions consisting of the callsign being sent in Morse code at 22 words per minute at a power level of 100W. Then one-second dashes are sent at power levels of 100W, 10W, 1W, and finally 0.1W. After transmitting this sequence, the station falls silent until its next slot in the three-minute cycle. Further information about this project can be found at *http://www.ncdxf.org/pages/beacons.html* and a map identifying the current locations of the beacons is also available at this site.

Ionosondes

It is possible to gain a view of the state of the ionosphere above by the use of an ionosonde. These instruments are often also termed *vertical incidence sounders* (VIS). There is a variety of instruments that have been used over the years from different manufacturers and with different specifications but basically they all provide the same function.

In essence the systems transmit a pulse of RF power that is radiated vertically upwards and the reflected signal is monitored and plotted on an ionogram (**Fig 8.1**). Initially the signal is reflected back by the ionosphere,

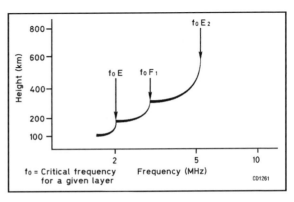

Fig 8.1: Diagram of a typical ionogram.

but as the frequency is increased it penetrates deeper into the relevant region and eventually passes on to the next ionised region where the same process occurs as the frequency is swept upwards. Eventually a point is reached where the signal passes though all the regions of the ionosphere and it is not reflected. The resulting plot which normally uses a logarithmic scale for clarity looks something like that shown in Fig 8.1. These ionograms indicate the critical frequency for each of the regions.

There have been many developments in ionosonde technology. Analogue systems were used up until the 'seventies. These systems all swept through the relevant parts of the spectrum, normally from about 1MHz up to between 15 and 25MHz. They generally used a relatively high power level, often up to 25kW. Sweeps could take anywhere between about 30 seconds and two minutes which gave them the ability to look at relatively short-term variations in the ionosphere.

Since the 'seventies digital systems have been used. These provide essentially the same information as the analogue ones but provide considerably more facilities and allow the data to be manipulated far more easily.

Although it is possible to set up an ionosonde at almost any location required, data from a number of stations around the globe are stored at World Data Center A at Boulder in the USA.

The UK currently has two active ionosondes, one at the Rutherford Appleton Laboratory at Chilton and the other at RAF Fairford. You can register to use the Chilton ionosonde at *www.ukssdc.ac.uk/ionosondes/view_latest.html*

Solar and geomagnetic indicators

It is possible to obtain information about the factors that influence the ionosphere and in this way it is possible to start to forecast what conditions might be like without taking soundings of the ionosphere. Several indicators are used, including the solar flux that indicates the level of radiation being received and the geomagnetic indices that give a view about the way in which the ionosphere might be affected by solar disturbances.

Solar flux

This is one of the major indicators of solar activity and gives a good idea of the level of radiation that is being received from the Sun.

It is measured by detecting the level of radio noise emitted at 2800MHz (10.7cm) and it is quoted in terms of *solar flux units* (SFU). An SFU has the units 10^{-22} watts per square metre per hertz.

To prevent different levels being quoted by different observatories, the standard is the reading taken by the Penticton Radio Observatory in British Columbia, Canada.

The solar flux is statistically related to the level of ionising radiation reaching the ionosphere, but unfortunately does not give an exact figure because the radio noise level at 2800MHz is around 10^6 times less than the intensity of the radiation used to create the ionisation in the ionosphere. Despite this it is a good first-order approximation, particularly for the F region that is responsible for most long-haul HF propagation. However, the best correlation with the levels of ionisation comes from the smoothed sunspot number mentioned in Chapter 3, but by its very nature this figure is only available in arrears.

It is possible to relate the daily sunspot number to the solar flux. A number of equations are available but the one given below is one of the most straightforward and sufficiently accurate for most purposes:

$$\text{Solar flux (SFU)} = 73.4 + 0.62R$$

where R Is the daily sunspot or Wolf number.

A slightly more accurate, although more complicated, equation indicates that the relationship between the two values is not totally linear:

$$\text{Solar flux (SFU)} = 63.7 + 0.728R + 0.00089R^2$$

Solar flux values can typically range from values around 65 at the sunspot minima to around 300 for short periods around the times of maxima. Low values will naturally indicate that MUF figures will be low, whereas high values will give an indication that the MUF will possibly be much higher. For 'good' propagation conditions it should be remembered that there should be several consecutive days of sustained high solar radiation with the absence of solar disturbances.

Geomagnetic indices

The state of geomagnetic activity is critical in determining the possible state of ionospheric propagation conditions. There are two indices that are used and which are related to each other. The first is the K index and the second the A index. Although different, both these indices give indications of the severity of magnetic fluctuations, and hence the level of disturbance to the ionosphere.

The *K index* is a three hourly measurement of the variation of the Earth's magnetic field compared with what are 'quiet day' conditions. The measurement is made using a magnetometer which indicates the variation of the magnetic flux in nanoteslas. This reading is then related to the K index and, when plotted on a logarithmic scale, the curve is virtually a straight line, indicating the relationship is quasi-logarithmic.

There are many stations world-wide that measure and log the K index. As the magnetic field varies around the globe each one has its own value, dependent upon the way in which the magnetosphere is affected, and therefore it is not possible to have a simple relationship between one station and a global K index. Instead the individual K indices are averaged around the globe to give what is termed the *Kp* or *planetary K index*.

The Kp index ranges in value from 0 to 9. Values between 0 and 1 indicate quiet magnetic conditions and would give rise to virtually no degradation in HF band conditions. Values between 2 and 4 provide an indication of unsettled magnetic conditions that indicate the possibility of some degradation on the HF bands. A value of 5 signifies a minor storm and 6 a larger one. Values through to 9 indicate steadily worsening conditions with 9 representing a

K index	0	1	2	3	4	5	6	7	8	9
a index	0	3	7	15	27	48	80	140	240	400

Table 8.2. It is possible to relate the K and a indices so that approximate conversions can be accomplished between the two values.

major storm that is likely to result in a blackout in HF conditions for several hours.

The *A index*, unlike the K index, is a linear measure of the Earth's field. As a result its values extend over a much wider range. It is derived from the K index by scaling it to give a linear value which is termed the *a index*. The approximate relationship between the K and a indices is shown in **Table 8.2**. The a index is then averaged over the period of a day to give the A index. Like the K index, values are averaged around the globe to give the *planetary Ap index*.

Values for the A index range up to 100 during a storm and may rise as high as 400 in a severe geomagnetic storm.

Although geomagnetic and ionospheric storms are interrelated, it is worth noting that they are different. A geomagnetic storm is a disturbance of the Earth's magnetic field and an ionosphere storm is a disturbance of the ionosphere. However, a magnetic storm usually, but not always, leads to an ionospheric storm.

Manual interpretation of data

It is often advantageous to gain an idea of what the solar flux, daily sunspot number and magnetic indices mean. For good HF conditions to prevail, one of the first requirements is that the solar radiation should be high and have remained this way for several days. This will enable the F2 region ionisation levels to rise and enable the MUFs to increase, thereby supporting good HF conditions. For this to occur, the solar flux levels should be around 150 or more for a period of several days.

It is also necessary that the levels of geomagnetic activity should remain sufficiently low during the periods of high solar flux that conditions are not suppressed and MUFs decreased as a result. Typically the Kp index should remain below a value of around 2. If this is maintained with sufficiently high solar flux levels then HF band conditions should be good.

Chapter 9

HF propagation prediction software

HF propagation prediction software can help you plan your radio operations. That is, if you are trying to contact the east coast of the USA, on say, 14MHz in October a quick look at some software will quickly show you that the afternoon or early evening are the best times. If you didn't know that you could end up calling CQ for hours and get nowhere.

There are a number of ways of finding out what band is open to where and when and in this chapter we look at some of the propagation prediction programs available.

VOACAP

VOACAP stands for the Voice of America Coverage Analysis Program. It is an ionospheric model predicting the expected performance of HF transmissions. It takes into account lots of different parameters to support you in the planning and operation of long-distance amateur contacts.

In the 1920s and 1930s amateurs and professionals discovered HF and DX communications. In the late 1930s, a considerable effort was made in the USA and other countries to investigate ionospheric parameters and determine their effect on radio waves and the associated reliability of HF circuits.

This analysis and research extended for more than half a century. In 1978, the Institute for Telecommunication Sciences of the National Telecommunications and Information Administration (NTIA/ITS) released the Ionospheric Communications Analysis and Prediction program, or IONCAP for short.

IONCAP allowed scientists and engineers to get propagation prediction results in a few minutes with greater accuracy.

The Voice of America (VOA) funded the US Naval Research Laboratory (NRL) to make changes to the IONCAP methodology, and renamed it VOACAP to avoid confusion.

This early version of VOACAP was completed in April 1993 and represented more than 50 years of US HF research and development. We can thank George Lane and Greg Hand for bringing us such a useful resource.

VOACAP is PC-based software and very capable, but it does need a fair bit of understanding to get the most out of it.

Nevertheless, as it is free it is worth downloading. You can find out more at *www.voacap.com* but make sure you read the tutorials, especially the one entitled 'Ten Common Mistakes in Using VOACAP'.

One important point: make sure you use the smoothed sunspot number (SSN) with VOACAP and other VOACAP-based programs. This can be obtained via a link at voacap.com. The SSN is recommended by VOACAP's authors as it is more accurate than predictions based on the day-to-day variations in the actual sunspot number.

Luckily, there is now an easier way of using VOACAP that doesn't involve running it on your own PC.

VOACAP Online

The amateur community is indebted to Jari Perkiömäki, OH6BG, James Watson, HZ1JW, and Juho Juopperi, OH8GLV, the brains behind VOACAP Online at *www.voacap.com*

VOACAP Online is a web-based HF propagation prediction engine that uses the excellent VOACAP software as its back end. It can make HF propagation predictions between any two points on the globe.

You just enter the coordinates of the transmitter and receiver sites and VOACAP Online uses the Voice of America Coverage Analysis Program (VOACAP) to calculate the maximum usable frequency (MUF) of the HF path between the sites. The site displays a 'circuit reliability' graph that indicates the probability of achieving an SSB or CW-grade transmission between the transmitter and the receiver.

If you're not sure of a transmitter's or receiver's coordinates, you can also use the Google Maps-based QTH locator to obtain the information, dragging a pointer around the map to show where you live and where you wish to work.

The software can then show you a 'rosette' for each hour of the day and each band (**Fig 9.1**). It is colour-coded to show you the probability of being able to make a contact on each of the amateur bands.

Pressing 'Run prediction!' will also give you a 'Circuit Reliability' graph that

Fig 9.1: VOACAP Online allows you to produce probability charts for paths from your own location.

shows you the best band to use in more detail. Another option gives you an area coverage map, based on your own location (**Fig 9.2**). VOACAP Online is very configureable, giving you the option to change the antenna type at each end of the circuit, as well as power and the mode being used.

VOACAP Online also has a propagation planner, which is a visual tool for HF contesters and DXers, plus a DX charts tool for predictions for upcoming DXpeditions.

Fig 9.2: VOACAP Online also allows you to produce coverage charts for paths from your own location.

We've barely scratched the surface of what you can do with VOACAP Online, but there are some other options. Other people have written software that uses the same VOACAP engine, so if you do want to have your own PC-based prediction software there are plenty to choose from. Here are some options:

VOAProp by G4ILO

VOAProp (**Fig 9..3**), written by Julian Moss, G4ILO, who is sadly now a silent key, is free and works with VOACAP to give a visual display of HF paths

Fig 9.3: VOAProp is an excellent free PC program for predictions.

on your Windows-based PC. VOAProp shows you typical propagation for a given hour of the day during a given month. The propagation is shown as expected signal strengths to be received from different parts of the world, plotted on a world map. It can also display daily point-to-point propagation charts showing the best frequency and time of day for communications with a particular location.

It is very easy to use and has a very neat graphical interface. It can also be configured to show you in real time which world-wide International Beacon Project (IBP) beacon is operating. It will also show you the sunset / sunrise terminator on the globe. See ***www.g4ilo.com/voaprop.html***

HamCap

HamCAP (**Fig 9.4**), by Alex Shovkoplyas, VE3NEA, is a compact freeware interface program to VOACAP, incorporating both graphical point-to-point and area coverage predictions. The program is pretty much self-contained;

Fig 9.4: A HamCap screen, showing signal-to-noise ratio against time and frequency.

the only thing you probably need to get from the Internet is the smoothed international sunspot number (SSN), which you can get from the VOACAP.com website.

The program works together with VOACAP to give visual propagation predictions. It can also be used with *DX Atlas* (not free). It has a small unobtrusive window and can be adapted to suit any hams, from someone with a dipole and 10W to an amateur with a three-element Yagi and 400W. It has even been integrated into the *Logger32* logging program so that you can see your propagation predictions while using the log.

See ***www.dxatlas.com/hamcap***

ACE-HF Pro

ACE-HF Pro (***www.longwaveinc.com/ace/ace-hf-pro***) costs $199, but is one of the best prediction programs around. It has a lot of features and is excellent at working out the best time to make a contact on any given path.

ACE stands for Animated Communications Effectiveness, a coverage display technique originally developed for US Navy submarine communications. ACE-HF PRO is the system simulation and visualisation software written for amateur radio operations and short wave listeners

ACE-HF Pro can show a sequential series of coverage maps. When the maps are animated, a movie is shown that displays reception of the signal in question. This helps you see at a glance what operating conditions are like during the period you are modelling. In addition, all graphs and circuit analysis results can be animated.

The latest version of ACE-HF Pro introduced the use of Google Maps to display the predicted reception areas, as shown in **Fig 9.5**.

ACE-HF Pro might not be suitable for complete beginners, but it can be very useful for more experienced amateurs. It is particularly good at letting you see the best time to work a DX station on each band.

Fig 9.5: ACE-HF will let you do point-to-point or area predictions, with the results displayed on Google Maps.

W6ELProp

W6ELProp predicts ionospheric (sky wave) propagation between any two locations on the earth on frequencies between 3 and 30 MHz. This is another free PC program, written by Sheldon Shallon, W6EL, but it uses a different ionospheric model to VOACAP. The program is getting a little old now, but it is very good and can be better at predicting 80m propagation openings than VOACAP, which was never designed to work at frequencies as low as 3.5MHz.

It is now unlikely to be updated and it can be a little clunky when running it on a modern Windows-based PC. But as it is free it is worth a try.

See ***www.qsl.net/w6elprop***

ASAPS v6

The IPS Advanced Stand Alone Prediction System (ASAPS) from Australia allows the prediction of sky-wave communications conditions in the HF and low VHF radio spectrum.

It is based on an ionospheric model developed by Space Weather Services within the Australian Bureau of Meteorology and ITU-R / CCIR models (Rec. ITU-R P.533-10, Rec. ITU-R P.372-10 and CCIR Report 322).

IPS says ASAPS has been purchased by more than 3000 customers typically working in support of aviation, defence and emergency services. It adds that the ASAPS prediction system is more accurate than other prediction systems because the *T index* is used to quantify the response of the ionosphere to solar activity. The T index is derived from observed values of maximum ionospheric frequencies and has the same scale as the sunspot number.

ASAPS predictions are especially accurate when they are driven by real-time T indices for the circuit or region of interest.

IPS derives the T index from making extensive observations of the ionosphere over several solar cycles and then plotting the maximum ionospheric frequency against the sunspot number. From this, it is possible to obtain a relationship between the two.

The T index can be best regarded as an 'equivalent sunspot number' – the sunspot number which would best match the observations made by ionosondes.

The authors say the T index is provides "superior parameterisation of the ionosphere's response to changing solar-geomagnetic conditions" compared with the sunspot number.

The full version of ASAPS costs AUD $385 (around £226 at the time of writing). There is a free demo version: see ***www.ips.gov.au***

ITURHFPROP

ITURHFPROP is a relatively new PC-based HF propagation prediction program that has been produced by the International Telecommunication Union (ITU) and is based on its Recommendation ITU-R P.533.

The interface and output for ITURHFPROP is quite complex and not for beginners. But thanks to the work of Gwyn Williiams, G4FKH, Chris Behm and James Watson, there is a web-based version of the program freely available for you to use. The trio have taken ITURHFPROP and have modified it to produce area coverage maps of predicted HF openings from the UK via the web (**Fig 9.6**). It can also produce point-to-point predictions for any two points of the globe.

You can pick any band and the software will show you the areas of the world you are likely to be able to work, the percentage reliability of making the contact or the likely signal-to-noise (SNR) ratio.

This is a great alternative to VOACAP.com and uses a different ionospheric model so it will be interesting to compare the two once the web-based version of ITURHFPROP is fully up and running.

At the time of writing, and as the software is developing, you can access it at www.predtest.uk

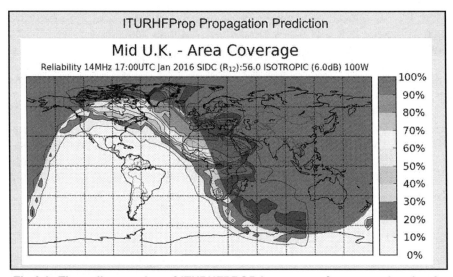

Fig 9.6: The online version of ITURHFPROP is a new software service that is running at www.predtest.uk

Others

There are many other PC-based HF prediction software packages around, but the above are the most commonly used. We suggest you start with one of the free ones, perhaps VOAProp, and see how you get on.

If you are in the UK you can also use the monthly HF predictions charts by Gwyn, G4FKH, that are in *RadCom* and also available online at ***rsgb.org***

Chapter 10

Tropospheric propagation

Although there are many radio signal propagation effects associated with the ionosphere, the troposphere also plays a very important role. It primarily affects frequencies above those affected by the ionosphere, becoming increasingly important at frequencies in the VHF portion of the spectrum and above.

Line of sight

Most communications at VHF might initially be thought to be only along the line of sight. Although under normal conditions this may ostensibly be true, even under these conditions the distance that signals may be propagated is extended beyond that which a direct straight-line model might be expected to give.

The reason for this is that radio waves are refracted as they pass from a region with one refractive index to a region with another refractive index, bending towards the region of the higher index as described in Chapter 1. The refractive index of the atmosphere varies according to a variety of factors. Temperature, atmospheric pressure and water vapour pressure all influence the value. Even small changes in these variables can make a significant difference because radio signals can be refracted over the whole of the signal path and this may extend for many kilometres.

An example of the effect that the changing refractive index of air has on electromagnetic waves can often be seen with light waves. Hot air above a heated surface such as a road or even sand directs the light upwards so that light from the sky is seen. As the hot air moves this creates a shimmering effect that can be easily noticed. A proper mirage can occur if cool air falls below a region of hot air. In this case the light waves are refracted downwards and this extends the line of sight. Tales are told of oases that appear in the desert as a result of this!

Radio waves are also electromagnetic waves and are affected in exactly the same way. There are very small changes in refractive index in the air as a result of slightly increased pressure closest to the Earth's surface and also as a result of the higher level of water vapour. As a result the radio signals are refracted around the Earth's surface.

The average value of refractive index is around 1.0003, but it can easily vary from 1.00027 to 1.00035. In view of the very small changes that are seen, N units are often used. These N units are obtained by subtracting 1 from the refractive index and multiplying the remainder by a million. In this way more manageable numbers are obtained.

$$N = (\mu - 1) \times 10^6$$

where μ is the refractive index.

As a rough guide the value of refractive index falls by around 0.0004, ie 400 N units, with every kilometre increase in height. This occurs under normal conditions and in a temperature zone. As a result it means that radio signals will be bent slightly towards the Earth's surface and will be able to follow its curvature beyond the geometric horizon. The actual values extend the radio horizon by about a third. This factor is used in most coverage calculations for broadcast radio transmitters.

Enhanced conditions

It is possible for the troposphere to provide enhanced propagation conditions that enable signals to be heard over much greater distances than would normally be possible. This form of 'lift' in conditions is less pronounced on the lower portions of the VHF spectrum, but becomes an important means of communicating over extended distances, particularly on bands including 144MHz, 432MHz and higher. Under some conditions distances of 2000km may be achieved with distances of up to 3000km on rare occasions.

These extended distances result from much greater changes in the values of refractive index over the signal path. This enables the signal to achieve a greater degree of bending and as a result follow the curvature of the Earth over greater distances

Sometimes the change in refractive index may be sufficiently high to bend the signals back to the Earth's surface. When this occurs they are reflected back upwards again by the Earth in a similar fashion to that seen with multi-hop ionospheric propagation on the HF band. In this way the signals may be considered to 'bounce' along the Earth's surface (**Fig 10.1**). This is one form of tropospheric duct that can occur.

A form of elevated ducting can also occur. This may happen when a layer of air with a high refractive index has a

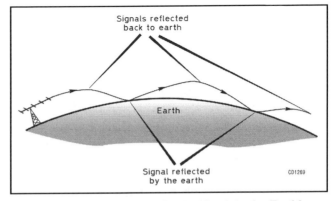

Fig 10.1: Signals may be refracted back to the Earth's surface which will then reflect them back upwards to give a form of multi-hop transmission.

95

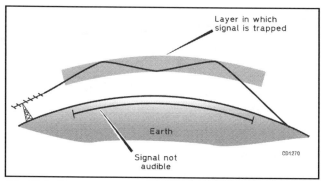

Fig 10.2: Elevated ducts enable signals to travel for extended distances and are not audible to stations underneath the duct, creating a dead zone for the signal.

layer with a lower refractive index underneath and above it as a result of the movement of air that can occur under some conditions. When this happens the signals may be trapped in the elevated duct and they may travel for several hundred miles. They may also not be audible to stations under the duct and in this way create a skip or dead zone similar to that experienced with HF ionospheric propagation (Fig 10.2).

Causes of enhanced conditions

The region of the atmosphere in which signals are affected by the troposphere is below altitudes of just 2km. As these regions are greatly influenced by the weather, it is hardly surprising to find that it has a major influence upon radio propagation conditions. By monitoring the weather it is possible to gain a good insight into what the tropospheric radio conditions may be.

One of the major mechanisms that causes a significant change in the refractive index is a *temperature inversion*. Normally the air closest to the Earth's surface has the highest refractive index. This is caused by the fact that the air is denser in this area and it contains more water vapour. Against this the temperature is highest closest to the surface and this tends to have the opposite effect, reducing the refractive index gradient. However, when a temperature inversion takes place, the hot air rises, allowing colder, denser air to come in close to the Earth. When this occurs it gives rise to a greater change in refractive index with height and hence better propagation conditions.

Temperature inversions can arise in a number of ways. One is when an area of high pressure is present. The stable conditions mean that air close to the ground heats up and rises. As this happens, colder air flows in underneath it, causing the inversion. This effect is particularly dramatic in summer when temperatures are higher. In view of the fact that high-pressure systems are normally stable and tend to move slowly, these conditions may last for many days. Additionally the greatest improvements tend to occur as the high-pressure area is moving away and the pressure is just starting to fall.

Temperature inversions may also occur when a cold front passes by. A cold front occurs when an area of cold air meets an area of warm air, and under these conditions the warm air rises above the cold air, creating a temperature inversion. Cold fronts tend to move relatively quickly and as a result the improvement in propagation conditions tends to be short lived.

It is possible for temperature inversions to be caused by a variety of other meteorological conditions. The temperature higher above the ground is more stable than that very close to the ground. As a result frosty mornings can result in the temperature of the air close to the Earth's surface being much lower and causing a temperature inversion.

After a hot day, when the Earth's surface cools rapidly, temperature inversions may arise. Another time to watch is a summer sunrise. This can give rise to a short-lived inversion, as the air higher in altitude receives the effects of the Sun's rays sooner. Also the subsidence of colder air into a valley can give the same effect.

Fading

Signals that are propagated via tropospheric refraction over great distances are subject to deep slow fading. This is because the air is constantly moving and that which causes the refracting and ducting may be blown around, leading to changes in the signal path. As the signal will reach the receiver via several paths and is therefore the sum of several different individual signals, these may fall in and out of phase with each other, leading to changes in signal strength.

Assessing conditions

Although it is possible to gain a good idea of what conditions may be like, it is only possible to assess fully which paths may be open by monitoring the stations that can be heard and noting the directions from which the signals are coming.

The easiest method of doing this is to monitor any beacons and also compare their signal strengths with the normal readings under 'flat' conditions (if they are audible at all then). Repeaters may also be useful for this but it may not always be easy as frequencies are often re-used and distant stations may be masked by more local ones.

Another useful indicator of a lift in conditions used to be gained from patterning on analogue TV signals. Now that we have digital TV this indicator is no longer available. An alternative is to look for distant VHF / FM radio stations that are otherwise not normally audible.

It is also worth noting that not all the bands are affected equally. Some may be relatively flat while a good 'lift' is under way on another band. Also conditions may be enhanced more in one direction than another, so it is worth gaining a good idea of the best directions from an assessment of this from the beacons. In this way the beam antenna can be orientated approximately in the optimum direction.

Another useful resource when looking for potential VHF openings is Gabriel Sampol's, EA6VQ, **DXmaps.com**. This collects *Cluster* spots for two-way communications on VHF and above and plots them on a map. As such, this means that you can get a very good idea of world-wide propagation, especially sporadic E openings that are prevalent in summer (in the Northern Hemisphere).

DXMaps.com has a similar feature for HF, but it is the VHF and up capability that makes it useful for enthusiasts of the higher bands.

Also take a look at Dave Edwards', G7RAU, *Live MUF* software. *Live MUF* is a *Cluster* Telnet client that attempts to resolve propagation modes from spots and also calculates sporadic E possibilities purely based on incoming data from the *Cluster*. It has *great circle mapping* (GCM) built in to the app for live mapping of spots. For more information see ***http://g7rau.demon.co.uk***

Another resource is William Hepburn's tropospheric ducting prediction charts at ***www.dxinfocentre.com*** These use Hepburn's experience as a professional meteorologist to predict potential openings on VHF and above across the world.

Band summary

Bands that are affected by tropospheric propagation are all affected to differing degrees, and in the same way that each of the HF bands had its own characteristics, the same is also true for those in the VHF, UHF and higher portions of the spectrum.

6m (UK allocation 50 – 52MHz, US allocation 50 – 54MHz)

This is the lowest amateur allocation in the VHF portion of the spectrum. At the peak of the solar cycle the MUFs may exceed 50MHz and under these conditions world-wide communications are possible via F2 ionospheric propagation. It is also commonly affected by sporadic E propagation, especially in summer in temperature latitudes. It is also used for meteor scatter, auroral propagation and EME (moonbounce). Being comparatively low in frequency it is not greatly affected by tropospheric effects.

4m (UK allocation 70.0 – 70.5MHz, no US allocation)

An allocation at 70MHz is becoming available to more and more countries and this means that international two-way contacts can be made. The band can be affected by sporadic E and it is ideal for meteor scatter. Tropospheric effects are also more noticeable than at lower frequencies.

2m (UK allocation 144.0 – 146.0MHz, US allocation 144.0 – 148.0MHz)

The 2m band is one of the most popular of the VHF / UHF bands, offering a variety of modes of propagation. Tropospheric propagation can enable long-distance communications to be established when weather conditions are right to provide the enhanced refraction and ducting. Other modes, including auroral propagation, meteor scatter and EME, are also applicable. This is also the highest band that is generally accepted to support propagation by sporadic E. Openings can be up to an hour or so in the summer in temperate zones.

135cm (No UK allocation, US allocation 222 – 225MHz)

This band shares many of the same characteristics as 2m. Occasionally it has been known to be affected by sporadic E.

70cm (UK allocation 430 – 440MHz, US allocation 420 – 450MHz)

Although under flat band conditions very well-equipped stations may be expected to communicate over distances of around 300km, tropospheric refraction is more pronounced on this band than on the lower frequencies and it forms the main method of extended-range communications. Ducting can support contacts up to distances of around 2000km and the all-water path between California and Hawaii has enabled extended distances of around 4000km to be achieved on a few occasions. The band also supports EME propagation. Some auroral and meteor scatter propagation may be possible at times.

33cm (No UK allocation, US allocation 902 – 928MHz)
The main way in which extended distances may be covered on this band is by tropospheric lifts and enhancements. Maximum distances tend to be around 1500km.

Higher frequencies
As the frequencies rise, so the achievable distances tend to fall as a result of increasing path losses. Despite this, distances of around 1500km may be achieved on all bands up to 10GHz. Above this frequency attenuation from atmospheric water vapour starts to become significant and, although long distances are possible, they are not as great as on the lower-frequency bands.

Troposcatter
Tropospheric scatter is sometimes used for communications over distances of up to about 800km. It can be used almost regardless of the conditions, although signal strengths are normally very low. This means that high powers, high antenna gains and sensitive receivers are required. This method of propagation is often used commercially, normally on frequencies above 500MHz. It provides a reliable method of communications and is much cheaper than using satellites. In fact it provides much of the data communications for the oil rigs in the North Sea off the coast of the UK when they need to communicate with stations on the mainland.

This form of propagation relies on the fact that there are areas of slightly different dielectric constant in the atmosphere at an altitude of between 2 and 5km. Even dust in the atmosphere at these heights adds to the reflection of the signal. A transmitter launches a high-power signal, most of which passes through the atmosphere into outer space. However, a small amount is scattered when is passes through this area of the troposphere, and passes back to Earth at a distant point as shown in **Fig 10.3**. Path losses are very high, and the angles through which signals can be reflected are normally small.

The area within which the

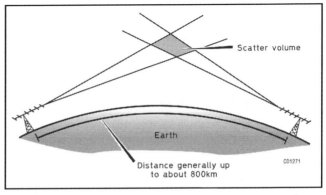

Fig 10.3: The mechanism by which troposcatter can be used.

scattering takes place is called the *scatter volume*, and its size is dependent upon the gain of the antennas used at either end. In view of the fact that scattering takes place over a large volume, the received signal will have travelled over a variety of paths. This tends to 'blur' the signal and make high-speed data transmissions difficult.

It is also found that there are large short-term variations in the signal as a result of turbulence and changes in the scatter volume. As a result, commercial systems employing this type of propagation use multiple-diversity systems. This is achieved by using vertical and horizontally polarised antennas as well as different scatter volumes (*angle diversity*) and different frequencies (*frequency diversity*). Control of these systems is normally undertaken by computers. In this way such systems can run automatically, giving high degrees of reliability.

Attenuation by the atmosphere

In the case of transmissions in the VHF section of the spectrum, atmospheric conditions like rain and fog have little effect on the signals. However, as the frequency increases, the atmosphere has a much greater effect on the level of attenuation in the signal path and at certain frequencies the loss introduced has to be considered.

For most UHF communications the effects of rain and moisture in the atmosphere are not significant as far as additional path loss is concerned. However, as the frequencies rise above about 3GHz the loss can introduce an additional degree of variation into the path. As may be expected, the loss is dependent upon the amount of rain and also the size of the droplets. As a rough guide very heavy rain may introduce an additional loss of about 1dB per kilometre at around 5GHz, and more at higher frequencies. The loss occurs for two reasons. The first is absorption by the rain droplets. The level of actual attenuation is dependent upon the droplet size. The second occurs as a result of the signal being scattered and, although the power is not lost, not all of it travels in the original direction it was intended. In this way the antenna gain is effectively reduced.

At frequencies well above 10GHz, attenuation due to the gases in the air may be evident and in particular water vapour and oxygen. This arises by virtue of the permanent electric dipole moment of the water vapour and the permanent magnetic dipole moment of the oxygen molecule. There are peaks for the components, with an oxygen peak around 60GHz, giving rise to an attenuation of around 15dB per kilometre, and a lower peak at just over 100GHz of just under 2dB per kilometre. Water vapour losses rise steadily with frequency but peak just below 200GHz, introducing a loss of nearly 40dB per kilometre. For most amateur operation these effects are unlikely to be of any significance.

Rainscatter

Having just said that water vapour can cause attenuation at higher frequencies, perversely rainscatter can be used a mode of propagation at microwave frequencies.

Rainscatter can extend the propagation of microwave signals to well beyond line of sight. With scattering from rain at 2 – 4km above the ground, the range can be several hundred kilometres. This is a common mode of propagation at 10GHz where rain droplets range in size from about 0.5 mm to 3 mm (drizzle to tropical downpour) – exactly the right size for the scattering of 10GHz signals.

Chapter 11

Meteor scatter

Meteor scatter is a form of propagation that is used with great success by a number of people. Primarily a VHF mode, it requires specialised operating techniques and high-performance equipment, but it is nevertheless capable of enabling signals to travel over distances up to a maximum of 2000km.

Its existence as a form of propagation was discovered in the 'thirties but it took until the 'sixties before it was exploited to any degree. Now it is also employed by amateurs who can use it to great effect with high-speed Morse. Radio amateurs have also adopted newer digital modes, including *WSJT, FSK441, JT6M* and *ISCAT*. These have made meteor scatter contacts much easier. Professionals find it useful for a number of data transfer applications, particularly when sending data from remote unmanned sites to a base. Its use came to the fore in the 'seventies as computers became more accessible and equipment control became more sophisticated, allowing for the systems to be controlled by computers and data to be conveniently transferred where no other suitable means was available.

This form of propagation relies on the fact that meteors enter the Earth's atmosphere and as they do so they burn up, leaving a trail of ionisation behind them. These trails typically occur at altitudes between about 85 and 120km and they can be used to 'reflect' radio signals so that they return to Earth and can be heard over great distances. However, as the area covered by the ionisation trail is small, only minute amounts of the signal are reflected and this means that high powers coupled with sensitive receivers are often necessary.

Meteors

Meteor scatter propagation naturally relies on meteors entering the atmosphere from outer space. It is surprising to note that thousands of millions enter each day (the estimate is about 10^{12} meteors with a total weight of around 10^6 grams). The vast majority of these meteors are small, and are typically only the size of a grain of sand. The number of meteors entering the atmosphere is inversely proportional to their size. For a 10-fold reduction in size, there is a 10-fold increase in the number entering the atmosphere over a given period of time. So most meteors are burnt up in the upper atmosphere, and there are very few that are sufficiently large to survive entering the atmosphere and hence reach the Earth.

It is possible to split meteors into two categories: those that are associated with meteor showers at particular times of the year and those that enter the atmosphere all the time, known as *sporadic meteors*.

Meteor showers

The fact that meteor showers occur periodically throughout the year is well known by both astronomers and meteor scatter enthusiasts. These showers take place at set times of the year and last for a day or two, and during them the number of meteors entering the atmosphere rises significantly. For some of the larger showers, the number of visible trails increases markedly, allowing the casual observer to see a worthwhile number in an evening. A list of the major showers is given in **Table 11.1**, and of these the Perseids shower in August (**Fig 11.1**) is probably the best.

Shower meteors are characterised by what is termed their *radiant*. This is the point in the sky from which they appear to originate. The radiant is usually identified by the name of the constellation or major star in the area of the sky from which they appear to come, and this name is usually given to the shower itself. Apart from the main showers detailed in the table, there are hundreds and possibly thousands of other showers that have been recorded, often by amateur observers.

The showers are thought to arise from comet trails and indeed most of them have been linked to specific comets. As the comets travel through the

Shower	Begins	Maximum	Ends
Quadrantids	1 January	3 January	6 January
April Lyrids	19 April	21 April	24 April
Eta Aquarids	1 May	4 May	7 May
June Lyrids	10 June	15 June	21 June
Ophiuchids	17 June	20 June	26 June
Capricornids	10 July	26 July	15 August
Delta Aquarids	15 July	27 July	15 August
Pisces Australids	15 July	30 July	20 August
Alpha Capricornids	15 July	2 August	25 August
Iota Aquarids	15 July	6 August	25 August
Perseids	25 July	12 August	18 August
Orionids	16 October	21 October	26 October
Taurids	20 October	4 November	25 November
Cepheids	7 November	9 November	11 November
Leonids	15 November	17 November	19 November
Geminids	7 December	14 December	15 December
Ursids	17 December	22 December	24 December

Table 11.1: Major meteor showers.

Fig 11.1: The Perseids meteor shower in August is probably one of the best for meteor scatter operators. (Image: NASA.)

universe they leave behind them a trail of small particles that orbit the Sun in an elliptical orbit. As a result, when the Earth passes through one of these orbits, the particles in the Earth's path enter the atmosphere and produce a meteor shower. As these meteors are orbiting in a particular direction they enter the atmosphere from the same direction and as a result they appear to originate from the same point in the sky.

Sporadic meteors

Most meteors that enter the Earth's atmosphere are sporadic meteors. They are from the space debris that exists within the universe and in our solar system. The majority of this debris arises from the vast amounts of material that is thrown out by the Sun into the universe. Unlike the shower meteors they enter in all directions and they do not have a radiant.

Although the density of the debris in the solar system is broadly constant (after meteor showers have been discounted), the rate at which meteors enter the atmosphere varies quite considerably over the course of a day (**Fig 11.2**). This occurs as a result of the rotation of the Earth. Meteors are 'swept up' as the Earth's atmosphere rotates into the sunrise, but their amount falls away as it rotates away from the sunset. The same effect can be seen as a car is driven in rain – most raindrops hit the front windscreen but very few hit the rear window.

As a result of this effect the minimum number of sporadic meteors enter the atmosphere at around 6.00pm, and the maximum number at around 6.00am. The actual ratio between the maximum and minimum is generally accepted to be around 4:1 but the exact figure is dependent upon a number of factors including the latitude at which the measurement is taken. It is found that the effect is less distinct towards the poles.

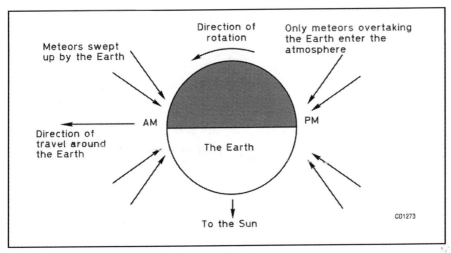

Fig 11.2: Variation of meteors over the day.

Other factors also have an effect, including the change of the season. This can be attributed to two main factors. The first is that the distribution of sporadic meteors around the Earth's orbit is not uniform. The density is higher in the areas of the orbit that the Earth passes through in June, July and August. The other reason is related to declination of the Earth's axis. There is a 22.5° tilt of the polar axis relative to the Sun that gives rise to the different seasons, and as well the seasonal variation in meteor rate. Those areas at right-angles to the direction of travel will receive the most meteors, whereas those at a greater angle will receive fewer.

The combination of the two annual effects is that maximum-to-minimum variation is accentuated in the northern hemisphere where the two effects add together, but it is minimised in the southern hemisphere where the two effects tend to cancel each other. As might be expected, in the equatorial regions there is a crossover between the characteristics of the two hemispheres.

Finally, there is a small change of around 2:1 roughly in line with the sunspot cycle. It appears that the number of meteors reaching the Earth reaches a peak around the trough of the sunspot cycle, ie the two effects are about 180° out of phase. This means that there is an improvement in meteor scatter propagation when the HF bands are at their minimum.

Meteor trails

Meteor trails form as the meteors enter the Earth's atmosphere and burn up as the friction from the air rises. The meteors enter the atmosphere at speeds anywhere between about 10 and 80km per second. The trails then form in a region between about 85 and 120km in height which is around the same altitude as the E region in the ionosphere. The actual height at which a meteor burns up is dependent upon a number of factors including size, weight and the angle at which it enters the atmosphere. The greater the entry velocity of the meteor, the higher it will burn up.

When a meteor burns up it heats up to such a degree that the atoms vaporise, leaving a trail of positive ions and negative electrons. The trail is a very long thin parabola with the meteor at its head. Typically the trails are only a few metres wide but they may be over 25km long.

The level of ionisation in the meteor trail is very high, being much higher than that in the ionosphere resulting from solar radiation. This means that signals with frequencies up to about 150MHz can be reflected by these trails.

There are two types of meteor trail. One is said to be *over-dense*, and the other *under-dense*. The point at which they change from one type to another is taken to be an electron density of 1×10^{14} electrons per cubic metre. This actually corresponds to a critical frequency of 90MHz. While the electron density is used to define the type of ionisation trail, it is actually the way in which a trail reacts that is of real importance. The meteors that create the under-dense trails are normally very small, often the size of a grain of sand. Those that generate the over-dense trails are usually larger. Typically meteors have to have a mass larger than about 10^{-3} grams with a radius of around 0.004m to create an over-dense trail. Below these approximate figures under-dense trails result.

Since over-dense trails are produced by meteors that are generally larger than those required to produce under-dense ones, they are less frequent, although they give relatively 'strong' reflections. Having a high electron density, signals do not completely enter over-dense trails and they are reflected. These reflections have a slow rise to the peak strength and a slow decay (**Fig 11.3**). Their overall duration is generally a few seconds but, during the period of the reflection, the signal undergoes multi-path related effects that affect their performance for the very high data rate transmissions normally used for professional applications. Nevertheless they are ideal for amateur contacts.

Under-dense ones act in a very much different way. Having a lower electron density, the signal penetrates the trail and it is scattered rather than being refracted. In this way some of the signal is returned to Earth. Again the portion of the

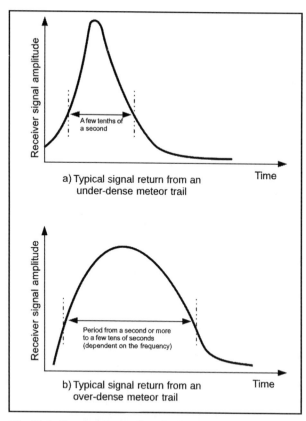

a) Typical signal return from an under-dense meteor trail

A few tenths of a second

b) Typical signal return from an over-dense meteor trail

Period from a second or more to a few tens of seconds (dependent on the frequency)

Fig 11.3: Comparison of typical signal returns from over-dense and under-dense trails.

signal that is returned is very small and very efficient systems are required. The reflected signal typically rises to a peak strength in a few hundred microseconds and then decays. This may take between a few hundred milliseconds to as long as a few seconds. This decay is attributed to the spreading and diffusion of the trail's electrons.

Of the two types of meteor ionisation trail, it is normally the over-dense type that is used for amateur radio communications and the under-dense ones for commercial communications. The reason for this is that the requirements for the two types of communications are somewhat different.

Frequencies

Like other forms of propagation, meteor scatter is dependent upon the frequency in use. This affects a number of parameters: reflected power levels as well as the burst duration. The levels of power returned reduce significantly with increasing frequency, as does the effective duration of the trail.

As a result the maximum limit for meteor scatter operation is generally around 150MHz, although some very dense trails have been known to affect frequencies as high as 500MHz.

Most amateur meteor scatter operation takes place on 2m, although 6 and 10m also provide very good opportunities and some operation takes place on 70cm.

The meteor trails last much longer on the lower frequencies, typically 10 times longer on 6m than 2m. This makes operation on the lower frequencies much easier, although the higher antenna gains that can be achieved with reasonably sized antennas counteracts the better reflections obtainable on the lower frequencies.

For the commercial systems that use the under-dense trails the maximum frequency is somewhat lower – about 50MHz. Typically most operation takes place between about 40 and 50MHz, although operation on lower frequencies would be possible. Below 30MHz interference levels rise as a result of the increased number of signals resulting from ionospheric propagation and therefore there is little operation there.

Paths and distances

Using meteor scatter it is possible to establish communications over distances up to just above 2000km. A minimum distance also exists because the trails are only able to reflect signals over a certain angle. As a result the minimum distance is around 500km. Between these two figures, the optimum distance is just over 1000km.

When making contacts the optimum beam heading is around 10° to 15° to one side of the direct path, as this is where most of the usable reflections can be achieved.

The gain of the antenna needs to be carefully considered because there is a number of effects to take into account. To improve the signal levels at the receiver, a high-gain antenna is desirable. However, it will have a much narrower beamwidth and the amount of the sky that is illuminated is much less. In turn this reduces the number of ionisation trails that can be used. Therefore

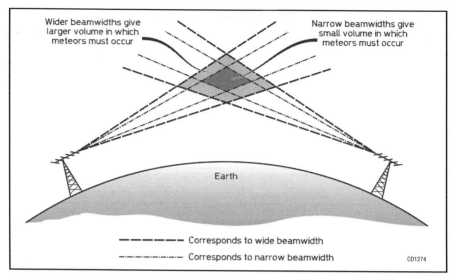

Fig 11.4: Effect of antenna gain on meteor scatter systems.

it is necessary to determine a balance between the improvement in signal strength and the number of trails that are required. See **Fig 11.4**.

Doppler shift

Meteor scatter signals are affected by a Doppler shift. This is because the point where the signal is reflected changes as the meteor moves forwards, and the trail behind it diffuses and reflection decays. This can give a shift in frequency of as much as 2kHz on the higher-frequency bands although it is correspondingly lower for the lower-frequency bands.

At higher frequencies the signals are only present for a short time, and this results in them giving an effect rather similar to a 'ping'. Signals at lower frequencies are generally present for longer and the effect is not nearly as noticeable.

Operating techniques

Meteor scatter requires a number of specialised operating techniques. The fact that communication can only be maintained in short bursts while the trail supports a reflection means that information must be transferred very quickly in both directions and procedures must be very efficient. Single sideband is rarely used because it takes too long, although it is employed occasionally on 6m. The more common way is to use very high-speed Morse. Speeds of 400 words per minute are used to enable sufficient amounts of information to be transferred during the life of a meteor trail. This is usually generated and read by computers these days. Previously tape recorders were used to speed up and slow down the signals for transmission and reception. Additionally contacts are often pre-arranged to enable stations to be listening on exactly the right frequency at the right time. It is essential to know the exact frequency because of the very-short-term nature of the signals, and accordingly there is no time to tune around the band for suitable ones. Furthermore any random contacts are normally made on the specific meteor scatter channels.

Although highly specialised meteor scatter stations are not needed for this mode, there are some basic requirements. Contacts can be made on 6m with relatively low power because the reflections are good at this frequency. On 2m where higher levels of ionisation are needed to affect the signals, the reflections are much shorter and higher power levels are needed. Typically power levels of around 100W at the antenna and an antenna gain of around 10dBd are needed. Coupled to this, a low-noise front-end is essential because of the low signal strengths at the receiver. In addition to this a means of sending and receiving high-speed Morse code is required.

A better alternative is to use one of the modern digital modes such as *FSK441* or *JT6M*, which are designed to support communications using very brief 'pings' from meteor trails in the ionosphere. JT6M, introduced in late 2002, uses multiple frequency-shift keying with 44 tones. The mode is known for sounding a bit like piccolo music and is optimised for use on 6m (50MHz).

These digital modes are very effective with weak signals.

Commercial operation

Meteor scatter is used for many commercial systems, although the increasing availability of satellites means that this form of communication is being used less. Despite this, it provides a very convenient method over distances of just over 1000km where real-time communication is not required and for less cost than a comparable satellite system. For example, it may be used for returning data that has been collected by a sensor of some sort at a remote site. It may take 15 to 30 minutes or possibly even more to send data as it is necessary to wait for suitable meteor trails. If large amounts of data need to be sent longer delays may be expected.

For a meteor scatter system it is necessary to set up two stations. One of these sends out a probe signal while the other monitors the frequency. When a suitable trail appears, the receiving station picks up the probe signal and sends a reply. Data is then transferred in packets, the receiving station sending out acknowledgements after each packet. When the trail fades and communications are lost, the probe signal is sent out again until another usable trial is detected.

This form of propagation is easy to install and operate, especially now that computer technology to control the system is cheap and easy to use. It also has the advantage that it is reliable from day to day and not subject to the variations of the ionosphere.

Chapter 12

Space communications

There is plenty of scope for communications using the Moon and satellites that orbit above the Earth's atmosphere. Satellites are widely used today and are able to provide very effective communications. There is also the possibility of propagation using the Moon as a passive reflector. Both these forms of communication are able to provide very useful means of propagating signals over distances well beyond the line of sight.

Satellites

Since the early 'sixties when satellite communication became an economic reality, its use has considerably increased. Not only are satellites used for applications such as communications, but also for direct broadcasting, weather forecasting, geological investigations, navigation (GPS) and much more. Whatever their use, there are a few fundamental concepts that are common to all satellites.

Satellite orbits

One of the main features of any satellite is its orbit. Its use and other technical requirements will govern the optimum type of orbit, and in turn this will determine many aspects of the make-up of the satellite.

To look at the different orbits it is first necessary to understand the different forces working on satellites. They are pulled in towards the Earth by the gravitational field, and to balance this they orbit the Earth at a speed that creates a centrifugal force that is equal and opposite to the gravitational force. Simple physics dictates that the lower the orbit, the stronger the gravitational field and therefore the faster the satellite has to orbit the Earth to balance the forces. Similarly, higher orbits mean that the satellite does not need to travel so fast. For a very low orbit of around 100 miles a velocity of about 17,500 miles per hour is needed and this means that the satellite will orbit the earth in about 90 minutes. At an altitude of 22,000 miles a velocity of just less than 7000 miles per hour is needed, giving an orbit time of about 24 hours.

There are two main types of orbit that can be chosen for a satellite. The most obvious is a *circular* orbit, where the altitude of the satellite remains

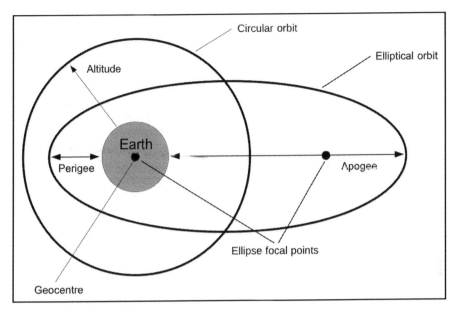

Fig 12.1: Satellite orbits.

constant. The second is an *elliptical* one where the height varies with the position on the orbit. See **Fig 12.1**.

One of the most popular types of orbit for many professional communications and direct broadcast applications is a *geostationary orbit* where the satellite rotates in the same direction as the rotation of the Earth and has a 24-hour orbit period. In this way it revolves at the same angular velocity as the Earth and in the same direction, which has the advantage it remains above the same position on the Earth's surface. To achieve a geostationary orbit it must be above the equator and have an altitude of 35,860km (22,300 miles).

There is a variety of altitudes that can be used for satellite orbits. Many are in what is termed a *low earth orbit* (LEO), having orbit times of 90 minutes or more, while others are much higher. Between altitudes of around 1000 and 25,000km the environment is not suitable for most satellites as the Van Allen radiation belts between these altitudes cause considerable damage to electronic equipment. Accordingly satellites are normally stationed below or above these altitudes.

There are a number of terms associated with satellite orbits. Any orbit, whether circular or elliptical, forms a plane that passes through the centre of gravity of the Earth (the *geocentre*). The rotation direction around the Earth can also be categorised. If the satellite is rotating in the same direction as the rotation of the Earth it is said to be *posigrade* or if it is in the opposite direction then it is said to be *retrograde*. The path on the Earth's surface over which the satellite travels is known as the *ground track*. This is a great circle track that has its centre at the geocentre.

Satellites with equatorial orbits obviously travel around the equator but for all others there are two points where they cross the equator. The point at which the ground track crosses the equator passing from the southern to the northern hemisphere is called the *ascending node*, and the one where it crosses from the northern to the southern hemisphere is called the *descending node*. For these orbits it is usually found that the ground track shifts towards the west for each orbit because the Earth is rotating towards the east underneath the satellite.

The height and velocity of the satellites are important factors. For many calculations the height above the geocentre is required whereas it is often stated as the height above the ground itself. For these calculations the radius of the Earth is taken to be 6370km (3960 miles).

Velocity is another important factor as already seen. For a circular orbit it is always the same. However, in the case of an elliptical one the speed changes dependent upon the position in the orbit. It reaches a maximum when it is closest to the Earth and it has to combat the greatest gravitational pull, and it is at its lowest speed when it is furthest away.

Elliptical orbits have a number of further points that are of interest. An ellipse has two focal points, and one of these is the geocentre of the Earth. Additionally there are two other points, one where the satellite is furthest away from the geocentre which is called the *apogee* and one where it is closest called the *perigee*.

It is possible for a satellite to orbit the Earth in a number of different planes. The angle of inclination of a satellite orbit is shown in **Fig 12.2**. It is the angle between a line perpendicular to the plane of the orbit and a line passing through the poles. This means that an orbit directly above the equator will have an inclination of 0° (or 180°), and one passing over the poles will have an angle of 90°. Those orbits above the equator are generally called *equatorial orbits*, while those above the poles are called *polar orbits*.

The angle of elevation of a satellite is also of great importance because the ground station will only be able to maintain contact with the satellite while it is in view. If the angle it appears above the horizontal is too small then the line-of-sight path may be obstructed by a ground-based object. Some additional loss may also be incurred on the signal passage through the atmosphere in general and also the ionosphere, as low-angle

Fig 12.2: Angle of inclination of a satellite orbit.

paths will have a much greater path length passing through this area. In general it is accepted that an angle of 5° is the minimum for satisfactory operation.

In order to be able to use a satellite, the ground station must be able to receive its signal or be able to transmit one back to it. Normally this requires a directional antenna and, if the satellite is moving, the antenna must be able to track its movement adequately. In the case of geostationary satellites the antenna can remain fixed once it is directed towards them, but for all others a means of following them is required.

Ground-to-satellite paths

As signals travel from the ground to the satellite they encounter four main regions, namely the troposphere, what is often termed *inner free space* (above the troposphere and below the ionosphere), the ionosphere, and the outer free space. Transmission in free space has unity refractive index and is lossless (apart from the spreading effect that reduces the signal power over a fixed area with distance away from the source but without any actual power loss). The troposphere and ionosphere have refractive indices that differ from unity. The troposphere is greater than unity and the ionosphere is less than unity, and as a result refraction and absorption occur. In addition to this the ionosphere is a magneto-ionic region and this induces *Faraday rotation* on to the polarisation of the signal.

Faraday rotation

The Faraday rotation of a signal causes different elements of a signal to travel in different ways, creating some problems with reception. A linearly polarised signal can be considered as two contra-rotating circularly polarised signals. The phase velocities of these two signals vary in a magnetic medium such as the ionosphere and as a result the polarisation of the signal changes. The degree of change is dependent upon the state of the ionosphere and it follows the same pattern as that experienced for HF ionospheric communications, changing over the course of the day, with the seasons and over the sunspot cycle.

Ionospheric scintillations

This name is used to describe a number of variations of amplitude, phase, polarisation angle and angle of arrival that occur with signals. The variations occur in the short term (typically between one and 15 seconds) and they apply to signals well into the microwave region.

They are caused primarily by the variations in electron density arising in the E region, often as a result of sporadic E, but also in the F layer where a spreading effect is the cause. The level of scintillation is dependent upon a number of factors, including the location of the Earth station and the state of the ionosphere, as a result of the location, the sunspot cycle, the level of geomagnetic activity, latitude, and local time of day.

The scintillations are more intense in equatorial regions, falling with increasing latitude away from the equator but then rising at high latitudes in the auroral zone. The effects are also found to decrease with increasing frequency, and are therefore negligible when using frequencies above 1 – 2GHz.

Tropospheric effects
There are several effects that the troposphere introduces, including signal bending, scintillation and attenuation.

The bending in the troposphere is in the opposite sense to that in the ionosphere because the refractive index is greater than unity, and it is also frequency independent. This gives the signals a greater range than would be expected as a result of the direct geometric line of sight. Tropospheric ducting and extended range effects that are experienced by terrestrial VHF and UHF communications may also be experienced when low angles of elevation are used.

Scintillations induced by the troposphere are often greater than those seen as a result of the ionosphere. They occur as a result of the turbulence in the atmosphere where areas of differing refractive index move around as a result of the wind or convection currents. The degree to which the scintillations occur is dependent upon the angle of inclination, and above angles of around 15° the effect can normally be ignored. At angles between 5 and 10° the changes can often be around 6dB at frequencies of around 5GHz.

Doppler shift
With the fact that satellites, particularly those in low earth orbits, move very quickly, a Doppler frequency shift is apparent in many cases. With the satellite moving towards the Earth station the frequency appears higher than nominal, and then as it moves away the apparent frequency falls. The degree of shift is dependent upon a number of factors, including the speed of the satellite (more correctly its speed relative to the Earth station) and the frequencies in use. Shifts of the order of 10kHz may be experienced. As most satellites operate in a cross-mode configuration, the Doppler shift is not just applicable to the band on which the signal is received, but to the cumulative effect of the uplink and downlink transmissions. In many instances the effects will subtract because of the way the satellite mixing process is configured.

Path lengths and path losses
The path length to satellites can introduce some significant losses as a result of the distances involved. For LEO satellites this may not be significant but for those in geostationary orbits significant path lengths can be encountered. There is a minimum distance of 35,860km (22,300 miles) and this introduces a small but significant delay of 0.24 seconds in total for the uplink and downlink paths. This delay can make telephone conversations rather difficult when satellite links are used. It can also be seen when news reporters are using satellite links. When asked a question from the broadcaster's studio, the reporter appears to take some time to answer. This delay is the reason why many long-distance links use cables rather than satellites as the delays incurred are far less.

The loss due to the path length can be calculated from the formula:

$$\text{Loss (dB)} = 22 + 20 \log_{10} (R/\lambda)$$

where R is the range and λ is the wavelength in the same units as the range.

From this it can be seen that for a satellite in geostationary orbit the loss may be between 195 and 213dB for frequencies between 4 and 30GHz. The actual loss will normally be greater than this because this calculation assumes that the satellite is directly over the ground station and the path length is 35,860km.

EME

Although satellites are a very effective means of communication as an active transponder above the Earth, it is also possible to use passive reflectors. In the early days of satellites the USA launched a large reflector satellite known as *Echo*. This provided a large surface that could be used to reflect radio signals, and of course it was clearly visible from the Earth.

It is also possible to use the Moon as a passive reflector in a form of communications known as *EME* (Earth-Moon-Earth) or *moonbounce*. In view of the very much greater distances and the fact that the Moon's surface is not an ideal reflector, the path losses are colossal but nevertheless it is still a form of communications that many radio amateurs regularly use.

The Moon is around 385,000km from Earth. As its surface is not a perfect reflector it only reflects about 6% of the power that reaches it (see **Fig 12.3**). Added to the path loss for the signal travelling to and from the Moon, the overall path loss is around 251dB on 144MHz and 270dB on 1296MHz.

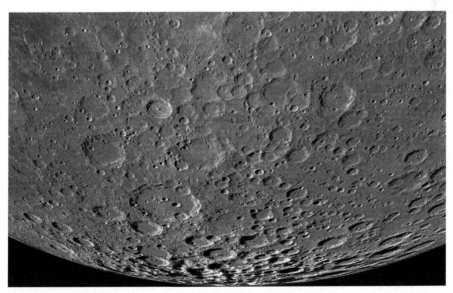

Fig 12.3: The surface of the Moon is rough with many craters and features that mean any signal reflected from its surface has elements with varying phases. The overall reflection efficiency is around 6%. (Image: NASA.)

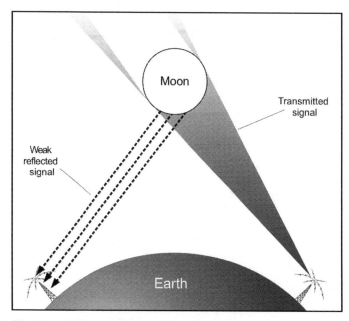

Fig 12.4: EME communications.

When using this form of communication very high powers, directional antennas and very sensitive receivers are required to overcome the losses. See **Fig 12.4**: the distance of the Moon and its diameter of 3475km means it subtends an angle of only 0.52° to observers on the Earth. In order to illuminate it with little wasted power either side, highly-directional antennas are required. Also these antennas must be completely steerable to be able to track the Moon's position.

Although frequencies as low as 50MHz have been used, it is more normal to use 144MHz, 432MHz or 1296MHz, where highly-directional antennas with very high gains can be used to overcome the path losses.

The first EME contacts were made using Morse (CW) and SSB, but more recently digital modes have been used to great effect. Joe Taylor, K1JT, is known in the scientific world as an American astrophysicist and physics Nobel Prize winner for his discovery with Russell Alan Hulse of a new type of pulsar. But to the amateur community Joe is better known as the author of the *WSJT* (Weak Signal Joe Taylor) suite of software. His *JT* modes, with digital signal processing, have made EME contacts a lot easier, even if signals are below the noise level. It is possible to make *JT65* digital contacts off the Moon on 2m using 100W and a single 16-element Yagi, but that should be regarded as an absolute minimum.

Any newcomer to EME communications is probably best advised to start with *JT*-mode communications before thinking about CW.

In addition to the path losses themselves the signals are subject to the same effects of Faraday rotation as encountered when communicating via satellites. At frequencies of 1296MHz and above it is not a problem, but on 432MHz it is believed that rotations up to 360° are common, and below this the signal may rotate through several complete revolutions. This may result in stations only being able to communicate in one direction at times.

An additional effect known as *libration fading* occurs because the surface of the Moon is not flat and the reflected signal consists of a variety of wavefronts, each with differing phases because the distance travelled by each one is slightly different due to the rough Moon surface. The received reflected signal is therefore a sum of all the wavefronts. As the Earth and the Moon are moving relative to each other the sum of these wavefronts is always changing and this results in a signal on to which is superimposed a rapid flutter as well as deep fading (sometimes up to 20dB) and some peaks. See **Fig 12.5**.

The relative movement of the Earth and the Moon can result in some degree of Doppler shift being added to the signals. This will vary according to the relative movements of the two bodies and also to the frequency in use.

Another problem can be that as stations are located at different positions around the Earth, a horizontally polarised signal in one area will be at right-angles to a horizontally polarised signal a quarter of the way round the globe. This spatial polarisation problem adds to the difficulties caused by Faraday rotation.

The use of EME propagation is a challenge but it can yield some excellent results. Those with the right equipment are able to make contacts with stations in many different areas of the globe when the Moon is in the right position relative to the Earth. In this way it is a challenging and interesting form of propagation to utilise.

Fig 12.5: After reflection by the Moon, wavefronts have a variety of phases which sum to give the overall signal. As these change with the relative movements of the Earth and the Moon this results in libration fading.

Chapter 13

Other web-based sources of information

The advent of the Internet has brought us access to an unparalleled amount of information. We can now access information that was previously unheard of. The Internet, coupled with imagery from spacecraft like the Solar Dynamics Observatory (SDO) and the Advanced Composition Explorer (ACE) means you can now better understand solar events and space weather.

We've mentioned a few sites earlier, but here are just some of the other sources you may find useful.

Space Weather Prediction Center

This website at **www.swpc.noaa.gov** (**Fig 13.1**) is a goldmine of information. For the RSGB's GB2RS news bulletin it has become the first port of call when trying to predict what the sun is going to do over the next seven days.

It is home to a 27-day outlook of 10.7cm solar flux and geomagnetic indices that will tell you the predicted solar flux and also the predicted Kp index.

From this you can attempt to work out if conditions are likely to improve or get worse. That is, is the solar flux index improving or declining, or are there likely to be unsettled days in terms of geomagnetic events.

So for the best HF conditions look for a high solar flux index and a low K index. Alternatively, if you are a VHF operator who revels in working via aurora a high predicted K index might be seen as a guide to possible auroral-like propagation.

The site also has a prediction from the US Air Force – look for 'USAF 45-Day Ap and F10.7cm Flux Fore-

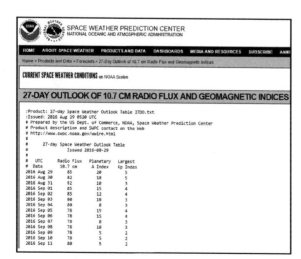

Fig 13.1: The SWPC site is full of useful information.

cast'. This can differ from the NOAA prediction and it is a good idea to look at both.

If you are looking for historical solar and geomagnetic date you can also take a look at ***ftp://ftp.swpc.noaa.gov/pub/indices/*** Here you can download information on solar flux, sunspot numbers and geomagnetic indices going back years. It can be useful to compare propagation at times of high sunspot numbers and for checking on the progression of the solar cycle.

There is also a whole host of other information on the site that should keep you busy for hours.

Solarham.net

We've mentioned this earlier, but ***solarham.net*** by VE3EN really is a fantastic resource for all things solar. As well as giving you the current solar flux index and K index (you might need to refresh the page to see the current ones) it also gives you easy access to images of the sun from the Solar Dynamics Observatory (SDO).

These allow you to see sunspot activity in near real-time. It also has plots of solar flare events and proton events, so you can exactly why the HF bands appeared to die! But dig a little deeper and you will find some other useful resources. As well as daily commentary on solar events, it also gives you access to all of the current imagery from the SDO spacecraft.

For example, clicking on the image marked '[SDO] AIA 131' will give you links to all of the SDO images, in different wavelengths. Clicking on the one marked 'AIA 211b w/ Coronal Holes' will show you the sun as viewed in extreme ultra violet. Coronal holes show as dark patches on the sun's surface (**Fig 13.2**).

If one of these is near the solar equator and rotating so that it is pointing right at Earth you can pretty much guarantee that you will have a high Kp index in around 48 hours as solar plasma escapes from the sun and hurtles towards us.

Fig 13.2: The dark patches on the sun, when viewed in extreme UV light, are coronal holes. This image was taken on 6 May 2016. (Image: SDO via solarham.com).

Fig 13.3: DXMaps.com should be your first stop for seeing what is happening on the 28MHz bands and higher.

DXMaps.com

DXMaps.com (**Fig 13.3**) is a fantastic resource for operators. Produced by Gabriel Sampol, EA6VQ, it has real-time maps of contacts being made on all the bands, from 136kHz right the way up to the microwave bands. It really comes into its own in the sporadic E season when you can see exactly where openings are occurring on 28 and 50MHz, across the continent and beyond. You can choose between a map view, or a frequency band map, or a straight listing of contacts. There is also a chat facility. You can even go back in time and see what propagation was like on a particular band at a particular time.

DXMaps.com is free to use, but Gabriel says that it costs a lot of money to run and he welcomes donations. If you donate at least US $20 or €20 you will become a *DXMaps.com* 'supporter user' and in return you will get the following privileges for a period of one year:

- Your callsign will appear marked on a yellow background on the maps;
- Your callsign will have priority and will be shown on the maps on top of other stations in your own grid square. If there are other supporter users in your square the priority will be shared and the report shown will be the latest at the time the map is generated;
- Unlimited number of queries to the DX database;
- Unlimited number of queries to the callbook and locator database;
- Unlimited number of e-mails with propagation warnings;
- Unlimited number of DX spots sent.

Furthermore, you will be making possible the implementation of new features in the future.

WSPRnet.org

WSPRnet.org is a website that shows the 'spots' received from people using the *WSPR* (pronounced 'whisper') software. As such it gives a good guide to propagation conditions around the globe. *WSPR* stands for 'Weak Signal Propagation Reporter'. It uses a computer program to send and receive signals and is used for weak-signal radio communications between amateurs.

The program was initially written by Nobel prize-winning physicist Joe Taylor, K1JT, and it is designed for sending and receiving low-power transmissions to test propagation paths on the MF and HF bands.

WSPR stations use low power transmissions – typically just a few watts. However, it isn't a two-way communication mode as such, in that you don't hold conventional QSOs. But the principle is quite simple. Stations running *WSPR* automatically send out a beacon signal on a given frequency. Each transmission lasts for just under two minutes and to make sure this all works you must ensure that your computer clock is set correctly.

Receiving stations around the world listen for your signal and, if it is heard, send the results via the Internet to ***http://wsprnet.org***

The end result (**Fig 13.4**) is quite fascinating as it gives you an at-a-glance view of real-time propagation. It is perfectly possible to find a 5W signal from the UK being received in Hawaii or Australia.

If you are interested in finding out more about *WSPR* I suggest you read the excellent article by Julian Moss, G4ILO, at ***www.g4ilo.com/wspr.html*** This gives you a good run through what *WSPR* is about and how to set it up.

One word of warning. Because *WSPR* signals are so weak you could be lulled into a false sense of security. That is, there may be a *WSPR* path open from the UK to Australia, but the signal is so weak that it would be virtually

Fig 13.4: WSPRnet.org can show you a near real-time snapshot of propagation conditions.

impossible to work the path using SSB. Nevertheless, **WSPRnet.org** gives a good snapshot of propagation conditions without you having to transmit a thing.

PSKReporter.info

PSKReporter.info started out as a project to gather reception records of PSK activity automatically and then make those records available in near real-time to interested parties.

The way that it works is that many amateurs run client software that will monitor received traffic for callsigns and, when seen, will report this back to the website (**Fig 13.5**). The way that this would be used is that an amateur would call CQ and could then (within a few minutes) see where his signal was received.

This system does not transmit any signals over the air, it just makes use of existing signals that are being transmitted by people calling CQ. This approach is different to some other propagation reporting tools, and has the advantage that adding more monitoring stations provides better coverage without consuming any bandwidth.

This can be useful in determining propagation conditions or in adjusting antenna and / or radio parameters. It will also provide an archive of reception records that can be used for research purposes. As such it makes another great resource for monitoring propagation conditions.

Fig 13.5: PSKReporter.info is another great tool for gauging propagation conditions in real time.

INDEX

An Introduction to Antenna Modelling

By Steve Nichols G0KYA

For many years the only way for most radio amateurs to work out how well an antenna design would work was to build it and find out. The arrival of computer based antenna modelling programmes has changed this. This book looks at the Free MMANA-GAL antenna modelling program that will let you design and optimise a whole host of antennas, and all on your PC.

An Introduction to Antenna Modelling has been written by antenna guru Steve Nichols G0KYA and shows you step-by-step how to input antennas designs into MMANA-GAL, how to adapt designs you are given and how to optimise your designs for the best performance. By the time you have finished you should be able to model a whole host of antennas including dipoles, the G5RV, the W3DZZ trapped dipole, verticals, off-centre fed dipoles (OCFD), magnetic loop antennas and many more. Computerised antenna modelling for many radio amateurs looks like a black art - needing expensive programs that look like you need a degree in astrophysics to get them to work. This book dispels that provides a straightforward way to design antennas with predictable results.

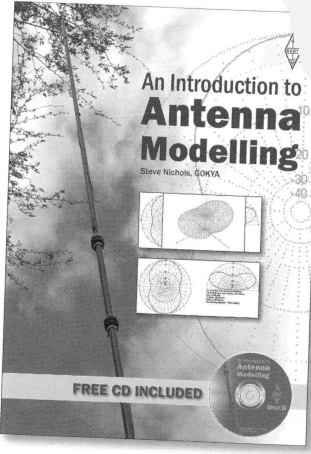

Building antennas can be hard work. You have to work out what you want to build, source the appropriate copper wire or tubing, measure everything carefully and spend hours putting it all together. But it needn't be like that *An Introduction to Antenna Modelling* provides an easy way to design and 'test' your antennas without ever lifting a saw or picking up wire cutters

FREE CD
This book is enhanced by the inclusion of CD that not only contains the MMANA-GAL software so you can get started immediately but much more. There are sample antenna files and event other antenna modelling software including EZNEC, MININEC Pro and 4nec2. There are also over 30 other amateur radio programmes included.

Size 174x240mm 80 pages
ISBN: 9781 9101 9300 6

Only £9.99 plus p&p

Stealth Antennas

By Steve Nichols G0KYA

The first edition of *Stealth Antennas* quickly became the 'must have' antenna book for everyone who wasn't living in acres of land. This brand new second edition has been expanded and updated and now provides even more for those with tiny postage stamp-size gardens, intolerant neighbours, planning permission problems or living in apartments.

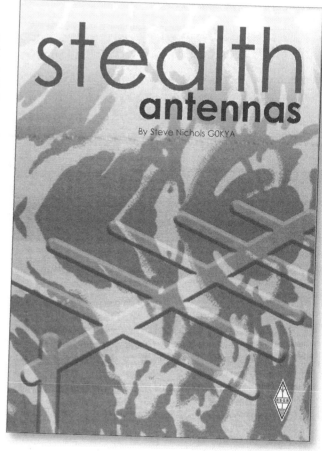

Many amateur radio operators are faced with the fear of interference being caused to televisions, telephones, hi-fi systems and anything with a plug on it. In these circumstances a stealth antenna may be the solution to allow you to get on the air or even the answer to your planning difficulties.

From using house rain gutters and drain pipes, or a magnetic loop in the loft, through to a tuned loop around the window frame *Stealth Antennas* provides a wide range of ingenious antenna solutions. Designs include magnetic loops, tuned wire loops, small verticals, zig-zag loaded dipoles and even reviews of a number of commercially-made stealth antennas. Along with new antenna reviews there are two completely new chapters covering Receive Antennas and Top Band Antennas. *Stealth Antennas* does not neglect VHF/UHF antennas. While easier to conceal because of their small size compared with HF antennas, what are the effects of mounting a VHF antenna in the loft? Roof tile absorption is discussed, as are the effects of detuning caused by copper water pipes or house wiring.

If you are able to put up a 100ft tower and 6-element beam this book may not be for you. For the rest of us, *Stealth Antennas* has dozens of original and ingenious ideas for antennas for radio amateurs who might have thought they were radiationally-challenged. *Stealth Antennas* should persuade anyone with an amateur radio licence that they can work the world without a beam, tower and linear amplifier.

Stealth Antennas continues to be the 'must have' antenna book for everyone.

Size 174x240mm, 224 pages
ISBN: 9781 9101 9305 1

Only £14.99 plus p&p

Antennas Mastered

By Peter Dodd, G3LDO

Peter Dodd, G3LDO has long been acknowledged as one of the leading experts on antennas in the world. For over a decade he has been the regular antenna columnist of the Radio Society of Great Britain's journal *RadCom*. This book brings together in a scrapbook format his work from this regular column and a collection of other antenna articles from over the years that have appeared in *RadCom*.

Antennas Mastered is packed with everything imaginable connected with antennas. Readers will find practical solutions that cover all bands, antenna types, ATUs, Meters, Software and much besides. Peter set out the intention in writing the 'Antennas' column was as he stated "The main purpose of this column is to address problems readers may have installing and adjusting antennas from suburban sites that may be regarded as a challenge; although any antenna subject that is considered to be of interest to readers will be discussed or described". This has held true over the years and readers will be staggered by the breadth of material covered in over 280 A4 pages of antenna gold.

Being a regular columnist Peter also updated and exchanged ideas with readers and discussions were often determined by readers' feedback and questions, making for some fascinating reading. Also contained within the *Antennas Mastered* pages you will find several standalone articles written for RadCom, the first of these being a method of modelling HF antennas using VHF antennas written in December 1972; long before computer modelling was available to amateurs.

Organised in the order they were written *Antennas Mastered* provides a fascinating look at the practical side of antennas and the comprehensive index provided allows the reader to access any specific subject.

Peter Dodd, G3LDO has created in his 'Antennas' column one of the best archives of antenna material available and *Antennas Mastered* provides this for everyone interested in antennas and the practical solutions they need.

Size 210x297mm, 288 pages,
ISBN: 9781 9101 9303 7

Only £14.99 plus p&p